THIS BOOK

THIS BOOK
The Truth About Drugs

MIKE ROCK

A GOLDEN RAINBOW BOOK

Second Edition

THOSE PUBLISHERS
LONDON, ENGLAND.

Second Edition Copyright © 1999 Worldwide

Illustrated by MAX

Typeset by Richarde Naison

with a little help from MIKE and James

A GOLDEN RAINBOW BOOK

Published by Those Publishers. P.O. Box 10059 London NW2 6WR

First © 1995,   Special Edition 1998,   Second Edition 1999

Printed in Wales by Y Lolfa

British Library Cataloguing in Publication Data

Rock, Mike. This book 1.

General Knowledge 1.
Title 615.4
362.1
082
ISBN 1 871 584 035

CONTENTS

Contents

This Book

Index starts on page 349

This book is written to really inform anyone interested in drugs, perhaps because they'd like to take some or maybe because they'd like to know what to avoid.

THIS BOOK AND THE LAW

This Book will discuss various drugs in detail. Some are currently legal, some are not. This Book works on the assumption that all illegal drugs could become legal someday!

Any advice or instructions given on how to make the taking of certain drugs more safe, which are currently illegal, should be seen as given in preparation for that day, or simply for general information.

Prices quoted for illegal drugs, included to make this study complete, are average, known, end user prices at the time of going to print, which would obviously go down should the drug concerned become legal.

Descriptions of drug effects are drawn from the author's personal experience or from interviews conducted with users, (effects can vary with each individual).

This Book

Special Thanks to

GAM
MAX
Richarde Naison
James Denny
Peter Taylor
Clive Corthine
Sean D'Alton
Michael Peaks
Neil Harris
Bob Welton
Chris White
Jaycee Conway
Dave Ebbut
Johannes Weerts
Hairy Mess
Jamie Firminger
Richard Playfair
Paul Needham
Bill Allan
Dave Pace
Jackie
CMW
Steven

For their inspiration and kindness
In helping this work to be completed.

Original Concept

David Rock

INTRODUCTION

All drugs should be banned. Drop that cup of coffee lady, you're under arrest! All you people in that chemist's, come out with your hands up, we have you surrounded! Doctor, you are charged with supplying, how do you plead? Latest News "Police raid local pubs and off licenses closing down a multi- million pound drug distribution ring." Does all this sound silly to you?

To some societies, past and present the arresting of people for smoking cannabis would seem just as ridiculous.

All through history people have been taking things which make them feel different. In some societies the partaking of certain plants is considered an important part in the coming of age process. These societies take drug experiences very seriously, and treat the taking of *special herbs* with great respect .

Many American Indians, for instance, partook of some very powerful substances at certain times in their lives yet they had no drug problem. These experiences had their place and held their importance, but when the time came to hunt the buffalo or do the things needed to survive, the herbs were put away.

Introduction

By providing their young people with the opportunity to experience the effect of easily acquired herbs and other plants in a controlled environment, they made it unnecessary for their youth to hide away taking drugs.

Our present society is the first to condemn people for taking certain substances, while condoning the consumption of other things. The result is that there are things available for sale in shops which are clearly harmful and deadly, while people are put in prison for supplying things which have never really been proved harmful at all. It's no wonder young people are confused when it comes to drugs.

"This Book" will tell you *the truth about drugs*. Together we will take a no nonsense look at where drugs come from, what they do and how they can affect the people who take them. You might already know a large number of the things in "This Book", but the bits you don't know might be helpful or interesting to you. Besides it never hurts to revise.

This Book is not to encourage anyone to experiment with illegal drugs, but being realistic it takes the view that while drugs exist people will be curious to try them. It also takes the view that people who are well informed will make wiser choices than people who are ill informed.

> The truth only hurts those who are living a lie.
> Read carefully and learn the truth about drugs.

DRUGS AND REAL LIFE

Before we start our look at individual drugs there are some things which should be said about the overall view of the subject.

The taking of certain drugs can create interesting and entertaining experiences in your life, but it would be sad to let drug experience take over your life. **If you take drugs, don't let drugs take you.**

Too much of most things can harm you. Eating too many carrots can cause carotene poisoning for example. If you are intent on satisfying a curiosity about drugs, you would be wise to compare the experience to a fun fair. Some drugs can create a fun place to visit but you don't want to spend the rest of your life on a roller coaster.

Drugs and Real Life

Our Indian friends mentioned before had a healthy attitude to drug taking. They were only for special occasions and they used the experience to learn more about themselves.

This doesn't mean it can't be fun and indeed if one is intent on trying such things, it is totally desirable that it should be fun, but first you should take the time to find out what the possible effects of a drug might be, (by reading This Book carefully for instance).

Don't jump into doing something you have no idea about.

If after careful consideration you do decide to try something, **don't over do it**! Start with small amounts, whatever it is you intend to try. Get the feel of it before you go further. Provide yourself with a relaxed atmosphere. Don't take something you've never tried and drive a car for instance. If you have no idea how this experience will affect you, be ready to just sit back comfortably and watch what happens. Ask a friend, not partaking, to stay with you and keep you out of trouble.

Take this advice and you'll have no accidents, you won't jump off any buildings, you won't get hit by an oncoming car or train, and you won't die of an overdose. (Oh!, and if you feel like trying to fly, DO IT FROM THE GROUND UP !)

ADDICTION

One of the main reasons for much of the confusion which surrounds drugs is the fact that the word "*drugs*" can refer to such a large number of different things.

The person advocating that drug addicts have no place in society would not be referring to all the people addicted to Caffeine, yet they fall under the definition of drug addicts too. Also, the lumping of all these things under one umbrella definition is an invitation to mistake one for the other. Yet they are all *very different* from each other. Before we start to look at separate drugs in detail it will help make things more clear if we discuss what certain types of drugs do.

Addiction

Let's first consider **VERY ADDICTIVE DRUGS**.

There are some drugs which create in the user a need for the drug. This is a need which is different from just enjoying something you might like to try again. These sort of drugs can create a situation where a person continues to take what they wish they could stop taking. When this happens you are no longer taking the drug, it's the drug which is taking you. It may then require an extreme act of will on your part to reclaim control of your life. There are many who can't seem to muster the will power required to stop taking such drugs. Consider for example the number of people who would like to stop smoking tobacco, but continue doing so. This is because tobacco is very addictive.

Some drugs become an obsession with people, to the extent that they live just to take the drug.

There are certain drugs which are good at making themselves the most important aspect of the user's life. When a drug becomes the most important thing in a person's life, then we can safely say that this person is addicted.

This Book

Let's take a brief look at how **VERY ADDICTIVE DRUGS** *work.*

VERY ADDICTIVE drugs work by mimicking a function of the body which provides comfort. When this happens the brain senses the job being done and stops producing it's own natural comfort. The problem is, this counterfeit function lasts only as long as the drug is flowing in the user's veins. When it's effect becomes faint and spent, a new supply is needed to continue. The brain is unable to start up production of it's own natural comfort and pain killers immediately, so the user, feeling the oncoming gap of unshielded pain coming up, will make every effort possible to get another temporary replacement, (A new fix). To the addicted person the replacing of this stock can become the most important things in their lives.

For the addict's complete devotion, such drugs will provide *temporary* comfort, which it will be up to the user to replenish. These are drugs which have the ability to take over the individual's life, if one is not very careful!

Addiction

Now let's take a look at drugs which can be **ADDICTIVE WITH CONSTANT USE** *and discuss briefly how they work.*

These drugs have the ability to do the very same thing that very addictive drugs can do, but they need to be taken for a considerable time before they can create this effect .

Where a very addictive drug can take over the user's life quickly with very few uses, these drugs infiltrate slowly, needing daily re-enforcements to eventually take control.

To avoid addiction these drugs must not be allowed to build up in the body. Occasional use with weeks left between doses will not result in addiction, but these drugs can be **ADDICTIVE WITH CONSTANT USE.**

Now let's consider **NON ADDICTIVE DRUGS.**

Many of these drugs don't seem to be designed for daily use. Taken one day they can be enjoyable, but try again the next day not much happens and they are a disappointment. These drugs do not seem to have any designs on becoming the most important part of the user's life.

They can set off a reaction in the user's brain which provides a special event, where the depth of constant beauty can really be admired. They place a magnifying glass on reality and make the user marvel at the wonder of it all, whilst the next day one can easily live without them.

These sort of drugs could be taken once or twice a year, for instance, as a special treat, but not having them for the rest of the year does not cause a problem.

It's like going on a picnic, or to a circus, which you enjoy at the time but you feel no real need to repeat the experience until maybe next summer.

There are also some **NON ADDICTIVE DRUGS** which can be taken daily while causing no problems to the user. These are taken because people enjoy taking them, not because they need to take them, and stopping is no problem. These can be habit forming for some people, but the habit comes from *choice* and not addiction.

And the exception to the rule, there is one drug I can think of which is **VERY ADDICTIVE** and widely used but does not seem to cause it's users any problems at all, (except maybe headaches and nervousness for a short time when they stop).

Society divides drugs into two categories, *Legal* and *Illegal.*

What they have placed *where* bears no resemblance to any logic.

25

Addiction

Others, trying to make some sense out of it, divide addictive drugs into two categories, *Mentally* and *Physically* addictive. These terms are very difficult to clearly define and they can cause endless discussions on which drug belongs where, with no agreement being reached.

Still others divide all drugs into *Medicinal* and *Recreational* categories.

It is far more useful to divide drugs into the categories of

VERY ADDICTIVE,

ADDICTIVE WITH CONSTANT USE, and

NON ADDICTIVE.

These are meaningful categorizations. .

To help you at a glance to make these important distinctions "This Book" contains a code with each drug being discussed which you will find in the right hand corner of the right hand pages, (further information concerning the addictive nature of the drug will be available within each section).

What follows is the key to "This Book's"
ADDICTION CODE:

	NON- ADDICTIVE*
	CAN BE ADDICTIVE WITH CONSTANT USE*
	VERY ADDICTIVE* *(addiction can be acquired with few uses).*
	ADDICTIVE* *but not known to be harmful to health or well being, (except in huge doses).*

*Please note: This code refers ONLY to the addictive nature of the drug being discussed, read previous section for fuller explanation, starting page 21 if you haven't already.

	DANGER of DEATH from OVERDOSE (see next section)

OVERDOSE

Apart from knowing if a drug is addictive or not, it is also vital to know if a drug has a toxic level which might result in an overdose causing death. While it is true to say that too much of anything could kill you, you are not likely to make the mistake of eating a fatal amount of ice cream are you? But many drugs come in a concentrated form which makes the danger of overdosing very real.

With such drugs great care is needed to establish what a safe dose is. If no testing facilities are available to you, this can only be done by trying very very small amounts to begin with, if you are in doubt.

In addition to our

addiction code symbols
you might also find this symbol
Which indicates:
Danger of death from overdose.
Treat such drugs with extreme care.
Your life and well being may depend on it.
(don't miss the section on Powders page 59)

The Right Honourable I. M. Killjoy

DRUG CLASSES

Sounds like a positive idea. Classes people can attend to learn the real facts about drugs and avoid possible problems. Unfortunately such classes do not exist and so called *drug education* leaves a lot to be desired. The government's idea of Drug Classes is to rate drugs according to the amount of time in prison they can give you for handling them, while they licence the sale and distribution of the drugs *they* prefer to use themselves, regardless of the dangers to health involved.

As a result, their classification system is of more use to solicitors, judges and police than it is to the average person.

While we will mention the legal class the government has allocated to each drug we discuss, this should not be seen as an indicator of the dangers involved healthwise; also the non-classification of a drug does not mean that it is harmless.

Next you will find the punishments involved with the different classes as stated in the *United Kingdoms Misuse of Drugs Act* (1971).

Drug Classes

The present trend is to enforce more rigorously the penalties for supply and trafficking, whereas possession is dealt with more lightly, however, 85% of all drug offenses are for possession.

CLASS A: *Possession,* six months plus a £5000 fine up to seven years and unlimited fine.

Supply/Trafficking: six months plus a £5000 fine, up to Life and an unlimited fine, (plus extra time for money deemed drugs money not being paid as ordered by a court).

CLASS B: *Possession,*Three months plus a £500 fine up to five years and unlimited fine.

Supply/Trafficking: six months plus a £5000 fine up to 14 years and unlimited fine, (plus extra time for money deemed to be drugs money not being paid as ordered by a court).

Any class B drug prepared for injection counts as Class A.

CLASS C: *Possession,* three months plus a £500 fine, up to two years plus unlimited fine.

Supply/ Trafficking: three months, a £5000 fine, up to five years plus unlimited fine, (plus extra time for money deemed to be drugs money not being paid as ordered by a court) .

Remember that laws are constantly being changed and the legal status listed with drugs in THIS BOOK is that which exists as we go to print. If in any doubt, contact the Home Office.

Drug Classes

Road Traffic Act: Road traffic legislation makes it an offence to be in charge of a motor vehicle while "unfit to drive through drink or drugs", and the word "drugs" here includes prescribed drugs and solvents.

Customs and Excise Act: Together with the Misuse of Drugs Act, the Customs and Excise Act penalises unauthorised import or export of controlled drugs.

Pooling together with friends to buy drugs at cheaper quantity prices can mean whoever collects them could be prosecuted for possession with intent to supply.

The legislation providing the penalties listed above has been ineffective in controlling the use of the drugs classified A B and C. In truth, making these things illegal has produced a highly organised black market trade in response. While the legislators are set in their ways over their attitude towards certain drugs, there are others who feel legalisation with proper controls is the way forward, (see page 260).

You might well see the hypocrisy of a Member of Parliament discussing the penalties for smoking Cannabis, while he sits in a bar drinking his gin and tonic holding a cigar; and this might well make you feel like ignoring the law and rolling a joint. But while these laws exist, you do so *risking your freedom*. That sadly is part of the truth about drugs.

SERIOUS HEALTH WARNINGS

People who are ill and under medication from a doctor should always take care not to do anything which might make them worse.

As it is not practical for us to list all the prescription drugs and the possible bad effects of mixing them with other drugs, it is best to say, **if you are taking any Prescription medicine, do not take anything else**. (There are guide books in your library in which you can find the whole range of prescription drugs and their possible side effects.)

Also it would be unwise for people with a history of mental illness to take psychedelic drugs, which work on the mind.

Some drugs put people with certain disorders at risk. Our discussion on each drug includes a "precautions" section. These are general precautions which cannot take into account each individual and their health. If a drug's effect is to cause high blood pressure, like caffeine does for instance, then you will find it is "not recommended for people with high blood pressure" .

Mixing drugs can be very dangerous!

In books setting out physical training courses, most recommend a full check up by your doctor be carried out before you begin. This is wise advice for anyone intending to do anything which might change the normal pattern of their body's functions.

Each "*precautions*" section refers you back to this chapter to remind you that YOU are responsible for your own body. Only with a proper examination by a doctor will you know *what* applies to you and what to avoid. Please heed these warnings.

CANNABIS

What Is It?
It's a plant which contains
THC. This is short for tetrahy-
drocannabinols, (and if any-
thing deserves a short term this does). It's the THC which
gives the plant it's effect when taken into the body by
smoking or eating it. The leaves and dried flowers of the
female plant or it's resin contains the THC.

Other Names:
Weed, Grass, Hash, Ganja, Blow, Spliff, Dope and
Marijuana, Wacky Backy, Shit, African black, soap, rocky,
sensi-milia "Jack Straw (Draw)"and many more, (see
Connoisseurs Guide, Cannabis Round the World starting on
page 241).

Where Does It Come From?
Africa, India, the Middle East, Europe (particularly
Holland), Mexico and the USA. It can also be grown
indoors with grow lights anywhere in the world. It's ability
to enhance a person's mood was first discovered in India.

In the 19th century it was known to be a cure for headaches
and sleepless nights.

37

Cannabis

It was used by Queen Victoria, George Washington and Benjamin Disraeli along with millions of others.

Also it can be used for rope, cloth and paper. It's oil can be used for cooking, mixing paints and soap.

What Does It Cost?
£85 - £140 per ounce (28 grams).

What Does It Do? (more about it)
It simulates the cannabiniod receptors in the brain.
Makes people feel relaxed. Helps you think on different levels, enhances the sound of music and prompts conversations on the meaning of life. While you are using it, you might forget your train of thought, but once the effect wears off your ability to remember returns.

It is very much a shared thing. All around the world, long three paper cigarettes, hand rolled called joints or spliffs are made to pass around groups of people to smoke. Those not wishing to inhale the tobacco mixed with Cannabis in joints may choose to smoke it on it's own in a pipe. Or it can be cooked in food, traditionally in brownies, a rich brown cake, (see Ganja Recipe Ideas page 263).

It can make some people feel paranoid, while it can inspire others. Makes friendly conversation flow easily in groups, and gives you the urge to eat snacks, (*the munches*).

Cannabis

It's been said, "the only way cannabis could kill you is if a big block of it fell on your head from a great height".

It is recognised as an effective medicine for bronchial problems Asthma and other diseases, (particularly Multiple Sclerosis). Also it is reported by the Canadian Medical Association that Cannabis is the only drug safe to use by pregnant women, having no negative side-effects on the foetus. It relaxes muscles and relieves pain without the side effects of other drugs now prescribed to sufferers. 57% of doctors polled believed that Cannabis should be legalised for therapeutic use, (1994).

Relaxed or relaxing people tend to be peaceful people. If someone offers you a fight while you are stoned on marijuana, you are likely to suggest that they go outside alone to settle it, then come back in to let you know who won.

The Government estimate 2 million people use Ganja in Britain each year, (The real number is probably much higher).

It is a non-addictive drug.

PRECAUTIONS
Smoking Cannabis *with tobacco* can seriously damage your health.

Be in a relaxed space.

Do not operate any machinery and don't stand under a crane while it's loading big blocks of the stuff.

To be completely safe you should wait until it becomes legal or go to Amsterdam to try it. More on that later.

(see section on Serious Health Warnings, page 35)

Government's Opinion
It is banned, maximum sentence for possession, 5 years and an unlimited fine. Sentences of 14 years and over in prison for importation are being served now. Rated class B (see chapter on Drug Classes for details page 31)

The possession and sale of cannabis seeds is allowed. Some farmers are licensed to grow varieties low in THC, for textile use, (a recent development).

In 1998 The House of Lords voted to legalize Cannabis for medical use, but were out voted by the Commons.

Author's Opinion
The making of cannabis illegal is a mistake those ruling at the time made, which the people now ruling are afraid to admit to. Their concern could be that they don't want to shatter their image of always knowing best. Perhaps they are worried we might lose confidence in them if they turn around on this one, so people continue to go to prison for helping others to relax.

Quitting is easy,
I've done it loads of times.

TOBACCO - (Nicotine)

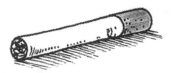

What Is It ?
A plant whose leaves contain tar and nicotine. Owing to
the industry it supports, it is one of the most abundant
plants on earth. It is smoked, chewed or can be absorbed
through a patch applied to the body, snorted as snuff or
even chewed in nicotine gum.

Other Names:
Cigarettes, roll ups (hand rolled), cigars, pipe tobacco,
fags, burn, ciggies, two's on that one, nicotine patch, snuff
and the brand names of tobacco products.

Where Does It Come From?
Main source: Produce of various countries is processed in
the U.S.A..

What Does It Cost?
£2.55 for 20 cigarettes £1.75 for 12.5 grams.

What Does It Do?
Smoking tobacco makes you want to smoke more tobacco.
Chewing tobacco does the same.

Tobacco

The craving for tobacco makes you nervous and uneasy until your next *fix*. It's the nicotine which is the addictive part. Once in, it leaves the blood system quickly creating a demand for more. An initial sensation of nausea is soon overcome.

This is **VERY ADDICTIVE.** It is near impossible to find anything that is more addictive than tobacco.

It is known to cause cancer of the lungs, mouth and throat, bronchial infection, heart disease, blood clots, strokes, ulcers and bad circulation. Some say it tastes good.

Most smokers will admit they would like to stop but they can't.

Nicotine patches are worn by people wishing to stop smoking. The patch provides nicotine to the body to compensate for not smoking. The dose of nicotine is slowly reduced with each new patch. This method of stopping does work for some but has a high failure rate. People also chew nicotine gum for the same reason.

PRECAUTIONS
Do not allow near naked flame.

Avoid during pregnancy.

(see section on Serious Health Warnings, page 35)

This Book

Government's Opinion

Completely allowed, with no penalty. Not legal to sell to anyone under 16 years of age. Health warnings are printed on packets, and advertising of tobacco on television is restricted to designs on formula one racing cars and signs at other sporting events.

Although an estimated 122 000 people will die from smoking related diseases this year, (1995) in the U.K., nothing is being done to prevent the distribution of this killer. It remains an important source of tax revenue and it's price always plays a major part in the country's budget.

Author's Opinion

Tobacco received it's legal status and acceptability in the late 16th century, long before the dangers of it were discovered in the 1960's.

This is another mistake the leaders of previous times have made owing to the lack of information at their disposal.

Again, for leaders now to admit such a mistake was made by those before them, might open the door to our asking, "What other mistakes did the people who set up the system make?" They cannot afford to have us asking such questions, so people get rich selling other people poison while the government continues to share in the profit.

CAFFEINE

What Is It?
An ingredient found in coffee, tea*, colas and chocolate. The worlds most popular drug, (*Dissolved in hot water to drink sometimes with milk and sugar).

Other Names:
Cuppa, brew, kick-start, cappuccino, espresso, Turkish, and the brand names of soft drinks containing caffeine, (see the labels).

Where Does It Come From?
Brazil, Columbia, Kenya and the Third World.

What Does It Cost?
£1 to £2.50 per 100 grams (varies according to variety) see your local shop.

47

Caffeine

What Does It Do?
Provides mild stimulation; can make you more alert. Lorry drivers claim it helps to keep them awake on long runs.

It raises blood pressure and was originally sold as a medicine.

It is **VERY ADDICTIVE.** Millions of people are addicted to caffeine, but many do not realise it because they never stop drinking it long enough to find out.

It has not been suggested that caffeine causes any diseases, but regular users who stop may experience head aches and uneasiness.

PRECAUTIONS
Not recommended for people with high blood pressure.

Taken before bed time it can keep you awake.

(see section on Serious Health Warnings, page 35)

Government's Opinion
Completely legal, sold to children in soft drinks.

Author's Opinion
One of the reasons it's not easy to stop using caffeine is because it's hard to find any real reason to quit.

KHAT

What Is It?
The bark of a plant, which is green and leafy. It can be chewed or made into tea.

Other Names:
Chat. Qat, qaadka

Where Does It Come From?
The Arab peninsula, Ethiopia, Somalia.

What Does It Cost?
About 50p a serving.

What Does It Do?
It is a stimulant which causes a sense of well being and makes the user talkative, hence it's nick name Chat. In the countries mentioned above it is as popular as coffee in parts. It is used as a social thing, much like tea parties are enjoyed in the U.K..

Khat

It can cause oral problems, such as infection and is suspected of causing some cancers.

It is rumoured to diminish sex drive.

It has been used for centuries in some Muslim countries, (Yemen and Somalia).

PRECAUTIONS
Not recommended for people with any history of heart conditions.

The oral problems are brought on by constant use, so avoid daily chewing.

Government's Opinion
Legal. An estimated seven tons comes in through Heathrow Airport, near London, each week.

Author's Opinion
The African's answer to coffee. It takes a lot of chewing but some occasional exercise might be good for your jaw.

It probably won't catch on with Western folk who prefer their highs more instant.

TRANQUILLISERS

What Is It?
A prescription drug.
There are thousands
of different varieties. Most are made active by something
called benzodiazepines. Comes in the form of pills, or can
be injected.

Other Names:
Diazepam, Lorazepam, Temazepam(eggs), Valium,
Librium, Mogadon, Halcyon, Normision, Tranx,
Nitrazepam, Benzos, Jellies, Ativan, sleeping pills

Where Does It Come From?
Drug companies all over the world, to be sold on prescription.

What Does It Cost?
The price of a prescription or 50p for a 20mg tablet of
Temazepam on the black market.

What Does It Do?
They make you calm, reduce stress and help you sleep. **If
taken for any long length of time, these can be VERY
ADDICTIVE.**

Tranquillisers

Occasional use does not cause dependency.

Prolonged use can cause increased aggression, excessive laughing or crying.

People who become addicted to tranquillisers find it hard to quit and experience illness and paranoia when they try to stop taking them. Withdrawal symptoms can be really horrific.

Taking these daily for a long time will put you in a daze. Weeks pass without being noticed. Much of you seems to function on automatic. Taken for too long you begin to seem like a zombie. You can do everyday things, but the spark in you seems as if it's missing. You can stop caring.

PRECAUTIONS
Mixing with alcohol can cause you to become violent.

Do not attempt to inject gel filled capsules; this can cause severe muscle damage and loss of limbs.

Don't attempt to inject tablets, (the chalk will badly damage your veins).

If injecting other forms, don't share needles to prevent the spread of diseases such as AIDS.

Can result in death if taken with opiates or alcohol, (from respiratory failure).

Mother's little helper

Tranquillisers

Can cause serious problems to people who have had hepatitis, liver or kidney problems.

Do not take during pregnancy.

Do not use on a daily basis, as sometimes prescribed. Use only occasionally, if at all, when really needed.

(see section on Serious Health Warnings, page 35)

Government's Opinion
Completely legal on prescription from your doctor. Millions and millions of prescriptions are written every year, most for long doses. Estimated at 1.25 million users each day!

(September 1995 Temazepams became illegal to possess without a prescription, maximum 2 years prison.) (The production of Temazepam **eggs**, became illegal October 1995.)

Author's Opinion
Tranquillisers can be very useful on rare occasions. There may be times when something is keeping you awake and you would be better off asleep. But the idea of taking these things on a daily basis for weeks on end is sad.

People on tranquillisers are easy to control which may explain the government's stance on this one.

ANTIDEPRESSANTS

What Is It?
Chemical drugs produced
by pharmaceutical firms.

Other Names:
Prozac   (Fluoxetine),
Amyltriptaline, Prothiadin, Zoloft, Paxil, and many current-
ly available or being developed.

Where Does It Come From?
Available from doctors on prescription, produced by firms
such as Eli Lilly.

What Does It Cost?
The price of a prescription.

What Does It Do?
These drugs have been described as mood elevators. While
they have been designed to treat psychiatric disorders, like
depression, they can also lift the mood of people whose
mental health is not in jeopardy.

Antidepressants

An American doctor, Peter D. Kramer, claims Prozac can make you feel "better than well".

While there are millions of people being prescribed anti-depressants, they are a relatively new thing and much still needs to be learned about their long term effects.

These drugs act on the Serotonin in the brain, a neuro-chemical which helps regulate mood and behaviour, much like MDMA works, (see page 179), but they need to be taken over a long period of time before any effects are felt, which leads to the claim that they are not a drug of abuse, (?).

The result is loss of irritation and negative edge. This can restore the capacity for pleasure, but many experience a loss of creativity in the process. Perhaps like the bit of grit needed in an oyster to produce a pearl, slight irritation prods us on to greater creativity?

The introduction of such drugs has prompted debate over the possibility that in the future, character failings could be corrected by neurological "smart bombs", designed for specific moods. One might take an anti-shyness pill for instance, to reverse an introverted nature. It is however agreed that it will be some time before such specific drugs are developed.

PRECAUTIONS
The elevated mood these drugs can create can also result in loss of creative thinking and unpredictable mood swings.

Large doses can result in death.

(see Serious Health Warnings page 35)

Government's Opinion
Legal with prescription.

Author's Opinion
Society seems to have this weird idea that things that make you feel good, for the sake of feeling good, generally should not be allowed. So, to get around this strange prejudice, the makers of anti-depressants claim that their products do not provide pleasure, but merely restore the user's capacity for pleasure.

Sounds like some clever double talk to me. What they are doing is capitalising on society's warped definition of what is good or bad. "Have a good time but make sure you don't enjoy it too much."

It's the same mentality that allowed doctors to prescribed whisky for medical purposes during prohibition, (see page 263, year 1928).

Antidepressants

While these *happy pills* can make you feel good with a loss of creativity, Cannabis, for instance, can make you feel good with an increased creativity.

Of course an increased creativity might result in anti-establishment ideas being expressed.

The people running things don't want us to think for ourselves because they feel it's their job to think for us. Our being happy is no threat to them, so long as we don't question their system. Meanwhile, while we smile, they can carry on with their destructive ways using our energy to rape the Earth and our ignorance to line their own pockets.

POWDERS

Drugs which come in powder form make it easy for dealers to mix them with other things. Dealers often do this to make more out of the supply they have, (these drugs are sold by weight). This is called *cutting*. Some cuts are quite harmless, like lactose (milk sugar), dextrose or various amino acids.

Other cuts might be less expensive drugs, like novocaine or even animal tranquilliser. Still worse, a dealer in a hurry might use anything at hand from talcum powder to washing powder to brick dust, rat poison, battery acid or any powder of the same colour they can lay their hands on.

Drugs cut in this way can pose a real danger to the user, (especially if they are to be injected).

Two part gelatin capsules with powder in them are likely filled by dealers after the drug has changed hands several times from the source of production. Each time the drug changes hands, it is likely to be cut with something to increase its weight and hence its value.

Powders

The result is that, with drugs which come in a powder form, it is very hard to know for sure what is actually there.

Recently testing kits have been made available in the UK to detect the presence of ecstacy. see page &&&&In Amsterdam, near (and sometimes in) some clubs there are small labs which are set up to test drugs, (for the price of a drink), to tell people what they have and to warn them of unsafe mixtures. Sadly apart from the 'E' detecting kits, no powder testing facilities legally exist in the U.K..

This Book Powder Poison Test
So for the wide array of powders being offered, where does that leave us?

I could say avoid all powdered drugs, but for some of you intent on trying something, that would sound like a cop out. This is not an easy section for me to cover. With the option of a proper lab test not being available there is no completely safe suggestion I can make here.

I can say to be safer, **never buy powered drugs from a stranger in the street.**

If someone you know and trust recommends a reliable dealer, sticking with them will make you somewhat safer, but to be even more safe I am left with suggesting something which many dealers might not go along with, and you might end up with nothing following this advice, but then again it's better to end up with nothing than to end up dead so I continue with the *This Book Powder Poison Test*

Here's how it works.
You only agree to make the purchase on condition that the person selling it to you shows you two identical doses from the same batch.

You will agree to buy one of your choice providing *they* agree to take the other in front of you. Arrange to meet them again the next day. Don't even think about using what you have bought until you see them healthy and sound 24 hours later.

If they don't show up, flush what you have bought from them down the toilet. If they refuse to make this test, do not make the purchase.

The "*This Book Powder Poison Test*" is nowhere near as good as a proper lab test, but it is an indicator as to whether you are being sold poison or not, and it will tell you how much confidence your dealer has in their product.

Another version of this might be, if a group of people are buying at the same time from the same dealer, you could always wait a day to see how the others are affected before venturing to take yours.

Does this sound to you like I'm suggesting that you use others as guinea pigs? Not at all.

Powders

A dealer should not be selling what he himself would not feel safe taking.

Also if a group of people feel happy taking something without knowing for sure if it's poison or not, that's up to *them*. If you wish to wait a day to see how it affects them, then that's up to *you*. If these people are your friends, and after reading this, the thought of them risking their lives troubles you, then you could always suggest doing the *"dealer takes it first test"* as a group.

Is it really worth all the efforts of taking these precautions? How much is your life worth to you?

Please note: A dealer passing this test once does not indicate that all their future product will not be poison. This test needs to be repeated each time a purchase is made to be effective.

Often dealers down the line don't know themselves what they are selling, but if enough people start insisting on this sort of test before buying, you can be sure they will make a point of finding out, and arrange group demonstrations of quality, (to prevent being constantly off their faces).

I could say here, to be completely safe, wait until the drug is legal; but if these drugs were legal, they would be produced to a set standard and you would know exactly what you were getting and not need this test.

COCAINE

What Is It?
It is a stimulant
found in the
leaves of the coca bush. Comes in a powder form snorted
through the nose or injected. It can also be rubbed on the
gums.

Other Names:
Coke, Charlie, Nose Candy, Erythroxylon, Coca, Snow,
Colombian Marching Powder.

Where Does It Come From?
Bolivia, Peru and Columbia, who's natives have chewed
the leaves for generations since about 2500 years before the
birth of Christ, with no apparent ill effects.

What Does It Cost?
£50 to £100 per gram.

What Does It Do?
Cocaine works by simulating the brains dopamine receptors.

It can make you feel very bright and awake. The thinking
process becomes very clear. Gives you a sense of well
being.

Cocaine

It is **ADDICTIVE** with prolonged use. It's been said "Coke makes you feel like a new person, and the first thing that new person wants is another line of Coke" It's been called "God's way of telling you you've made too much money".

Once taken, it acts quickly and continues for about 30 minutes.

Used daily for any real length of time it will weaken you and make you feel ill, causing exhaustion, weight loss and premature aging.

PRECAUTIONS

Frequent use can cause collapse of the nasal passage.

This drug has a toxic level, which means an overdose could kill you.

Its powder form makes it difficult to know for sure what it is you are taking. Powders are often mixed with undesirable other things by dealers wishing to make a higher profit. (see Powders for fuller explanation, page 59).

To avoid addiction, this drug should not be taken on a daily basis.

Avoid during pregnancy.

Cocaine

Severe liver damage can be increased because Cocaine is broken down and detoxified there.

If injecting, do not share needles to avoid spreading diseases such as AIDS.

Some people may be allergic to Cocaine.

A small amount once or twice a year will not cause problems to a healthy person but, all things considered it is probably best to give it a miss even if it does become legal.

(see section on Serious Health Warnings, page 35)

Government's Opinion
Illegal - Class A. Has been banned since 1920 in the U.K.
(see section on Drug Classes page 31)

Author's Opinion
Cocaine is highly overrated and over priced. It's a play thing for the rich, bringing with it an element of status. It's high cost is due to it's illegal Class A rating, and not connected to the results it produces.

The damage this drug can do to your health with prolonged use, and it's addictive nature, is eclipsed by the glamour which has been created around it. Cocaine's image has been carefully managed to appeal to the rich, like an expensive brand name. It's illegal status has created a huge industry which relies on the hype to survive.

CRACK

What Is It?
Cocaine in the
form of small
rocks which can be smoked. A treatment with chemicals
frees the base of the Cocaine from its hydrochloride, hence
it is called free base, (see Cocaine page 63).

Other Names:
Wash, Rocks, Free Base and Base.

Where Does It Come From?
Columbia, Bolivia and Peru.

What Does It Cost?
About £25 per quarter gram rock.

What Does It Do?
When smoked in this form, in a pipe or off heated tin foil,
the Cocaine reaches the brain very quickly. The result is a
fast rush creating a high which lasts for a few minutes .

In this form Cocaine is **VERY ADDICTIVE.**

Crack

It can become the most important thing in the users life because the need it creates for itself is so strong.

The comedown is depressing, and can cause aches and pains in the head and body. The user's system builds up a tolerance to the drug, which means the more you take, the larger the amount you need to get the same effect, (see Cocaine, What Does it Do ? page 63).

PRECAUTIONS
It is possible to overdose, causing the heart and lungs to fail.

Can cause extreme lung damage insomnia and paranoia.

Avoid during pregnancy. It has been noted that it is the only drug that can completely destroy the maternal instinct.

Anyone suffering from mental illness or who has doubts about their mental health should avoid this drug.

Severe liver damage can be increased because Cocaine is broken down and detoxified there.

Some people may be allergic to Cocaine.

(see section on Serious Health Warnings, page 35)

This Book

Government's Opinion
Illegal Class A (see section on Drug Classes page 31)

Author's Opinion
The processing of the Coca leaves into purer forms of Cocaine makes it more and more addictive, which is great for those involved in selling the stuff.

The selling of Cocaine is a huge business and the introduction of Crack is a marketing ploy to increase sales.

The native Altiplano Indians, for generation after generation, have been chewing the Coca leaves since at least 2500 B.C. with no apparent problems. It's use is known to cure altitude sickness, also it tones the entire digestive tract and promotes health of the oral cavity and teeth.

It is the greed of the Western World which has prompted the processing of these leaves into substances which create a constant need in the user. They want you as a regular customer for their over priced goods. More hype than high.

CAT

What Is It?
A stimulant made mainly from household substances which include Epsom salts, aspirin and car battery acid, with Ephedrine, a prescription drug from asthma remedies, which is the only controlled substance in the white powder mixture which is usually snorted.

Other Names:
Methcatinone, pseudo Cocaine

Where Does It Come From?
It was formulated in Germany by scientists researching appetite suppressants in the 1920's.

As a treatment for depression it was widely used in the Soviet Union during the 1930's and 1940's. When it was discovered that this is a very addictive substance, it's use was discontinued.

The formula was patented in America by Parke Davis' drug company which is part of Warner Lambert, in 1957, and lay on the shelf gathering dust for 32 years.

Cat

In 1989 Mark Mc Phee, a university student, stole samples (and the formula). With a friend Phil Pavlik he then started to distribute the drug.

They were both arrested two years later, but not before they had passed the formula to interested parties all over the country.

Making it is as easy as baking bread if you have the all important recipe.

What Does It Cost?
around £50 a gram

What Does It Do?
The effects are very simular to those of Cocaine. (see Cocaine, What Does It Do? page 63)

Some say it produces a longer and more enjoyable high.

Users have been known to go without sleeping and eating for long periods of time on this drug.

PRECAUTIONS
This substance is **highly ADDICTIVE.**

The powder form this comes in makes it difficult to know for sure what you are getting. (see powders, page 59)

This Book

Trying to make your own is dangerous and futile as the formula is vital for the right combination.

Governments Opinion
After recent consideration to be put on the list of controlled substances CAT has become a Class B drug. (see drug classes on page 31).

Author's Opinion
As long as the drug laws exist, there will be new things introduced to take the place of banned substances in a never ending line.

AMPHETAMINES

What Is It?
A powerful stimulant,
very similar to the
body's own natural
stimulants, Adrenaline and Noradrenaline. Comes in a
powder or crystal form which is snorted through the nose.
It can also be injected or taken in pill form.

Other Names:
Speed, Sulphate, Glass, Crystal, Billy Whiz and Whiz,
Purple hearts, Dex amphetamines, Pink Champaign, Black
Bombers.

Where Does It Come From?
It was synthesised in Germany in 1887. It was used in
inhalers containing Benzedrine. It is a chemical part of the
Benzine ring.

This is a prescribed drug, which is also produced illegally
in European laboratories, (and bath tubs).

Amphetamines

What Does It Cost?
About £10 per gram.

What Does It Do?
It excites the nervous system. Makes you more energetic and makes you talk a mile a minute, hence its name "Speed".

The day after taking speed can be depressing.

This drug can be addictive with constant use. Long time users can become over emotional, brought easily to laughter or tears.

It is an aide to lateral thinking, that is to say, you examine things from different levels.

Long time users can become irrational. They can attach over importance to mundane things and create misunderstandings within themselves and with others.

Occasional use can be a boost, but daily use will wear you out.

Causing the body to run at a higher speed for a short time can be an interesting experience, but running your body on overdrive constantly gives it no time to repair itself, as cells get burned out more quickly. Constant use will result in worn out body parts.

It can curb your appetite and is prescribed as an aid to slimming.

It was widely used by soldiers in the 2nd World War with over 70 million doses consumed by the British Forces! Modern armies today have huge supplies of Amphetamines ready for use, should a conflict arise. All aircraft carriers, military boats, military planes and each military camp has a large supply of this drug ready for use. It is used by the military to give soldiers more energy and to create a good feeling and high moral.

Most of what is sold as speed on the streets contains only between 5% and 10% actual amphetamine.

Recently it has been recognised that, when administered in small doses, this drug can be an effective treatment for Attention Deficit Disorder (ADD).

PRECAUTIONS
The powder form this drug commonly comes in makes it difficult to know what you are really taking, (see Powders for a fuller explanation, page 59).

Mixing with alcohol can cause liver damage risks.

Also, mixing with alcohol can give a drunk the energy to do stupid things they would have missed doing from falling asleep on drink alone.

Amphetamines

Causes liver strain especially in high doses.

As mentioned before, generally, Speed contains no more than 10% amphetamine. Sometimes however stronger stuff reaches the streets which poses a real danger of overdose.

Injecting speed can mean injecting undesirable cuts with it.

If you have a history of mental illness or doubts about your mental health, avoid this drug.

It can be cut with things that aggravate your nose and throat.

Too much can make you a babbling idiotic specimen, (Amphetamine Psychosis).

Avoid during pregnancy.

If injecting, do not share needles to avoid spreading diseases such as AIDS.

Don't attempt to inject tablets, (the chalk will badly damage your veins).

There is danger of over dose causing fatal damage to organs.

(see Serious Health Warnings, page 35)

This Book

Government's Opinion
Legal with prescription.

Class B with no prescription.

Class A for 'uncut' or prepared for injection.

(see section on Drug Classes page 31)

Author's Opinion
Question: How do you explain to loyal soldiers that you are recommending and administering to them a Class A drug to improve their performance?

Answer: You make it Class B and legal with prescription.

The military's reliance on this drug to snap soldiers into shape is far too great for them to ban it completely. It's current status allows the government to prosecute private producers, while still allowing the production of what they need on licence.

It's a clever arrangement, don't you think? How can you have your cake and eat it too? Simple, bake two cakes, or in this case make two laws, one for us, and one for them.

This drug can be an exciting experience to a healthy person, but if you'd like to remain healthy, don't make a habit of it!

HEROIN

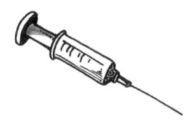

What Is It?

It's a powder which comes from the Opium poppy,
(Diamophine Hydrochloride). It is a product of morphine
which can be mixed with water and injected, or smoked,
(chasing the dragon).

Other Names:

Smack, H, Horse, Skag, Tackle, Gear, Pharmaceutical, Far
Eastern, Middle/Near Eastern, Pink Elephant, Tiger, Rice,
Dragon and also graded by numbers.

Where Does It Come From?

Pakistan, Afghanistan, Thailand and China. Some comes to
Britain through eastern Europe and southern Italy.

Heroin

What Does It Cost?
£ 50 to £100 per gram.

What Does It Do?
Opium works by stimulating and activating opiode receptors in the brain.

It creates a sense of warmth and well being. Users refer to getting a Gouch, Goofing Out, or a Nod, which is reaching a dream state of warmth and calm while still being awake.

This drug is **VERY ADDICTIVE.** A need for the drug can creep up on you with the result that a user may become addicted from casual use, without expecting it. Once addicted, the user will experience dreadful withdrawal symptoms when trying to stop, which include sweats, vomiting, diarrhoea, severe flu like symptoms, anxious breathing and sometimes coma. This experience is referred to as COLD TURKEY, which can last between 5 days and 3 weeks.

Users claim that going through *cold turkey*, as dreadful as it is, is actually a small problem compared to the lingering desire for more heroin, which can remain for years and years after.

Even after a 6 week period from stopping, one may still have trouble sleeping. This is where the psychological problems can set in, because the user knows even a small amount would afford them a good night's sleep. At this stage, even sleep induced by sleeping pills will leave the user feeling unrested and uneasy.

Being in an environment where Heroin is readily available makes it that much more difficult to quit. Studies have shown that 95% of the soldiers which became addicted to Heroin while serving in Vietnam stopped using the drug when they got home again. Being away from the place which they associated with the drug's use seems to have made it easier to stop.

The average rate of success for those attempting to quit while remaining in the area where their habit was formed is under 30%. This study indicates the strong psychological effect anything associated with the drug can have on the former user.

It acts as both a sedative and a stimulant. Providing the drug is not administered in excessive amounts it causes no physical damage to the body. It's hold on the user and the problems caused from not having it are it's main draw back.

Within the nervous system it acts as a pain killer, providing a counterfeit supply of endorphines. Endorphines occur naturally in the brain to relieve pain. While these counterfeit endorphines are there, the brain sees no need to produce it's own.

83

Heroin

Stop the supply of counterfeit endorphines and it takes some time for the brain to start up it's own production again. It is during this time, when there is nothing available to stem the pain of natural growth and body functions, that *cold turkey* occurs.

The taking of prescribed opiates (discussed in the next chapter) as a substitute for Heroin will only delay the horror of *cold turkey* which, from Methadone for instance is known to be much worse. There is no easy way known to go through *cold turkey*.

PRECAUTIONS
Sharing needles can spread diseases such as AIDS.

The powder form this drug comes in makes it difficult to determine it's strength, or to know for sure what it actually is; (see Powders for a fuller explanation page 59).

Users often suffer from constipation.

Pharmaceutical 100mg ampoules while highly sought after can be deceptively strong compared to methadone ampoules and can be fatal if substituted in equal amounts.

A too pure or impure dose can kill you.

To avoid addiction, this drug should not be taken.

This Book

(see Serious Health Warnings page 35)

Government's Opinion
Illegal, Class A, (see section on Drug Classes page 31).

This is the drug they use to justify all their other drug laws.

Author's Opinion
I've never met a user or a former user who recommended it. For what this drug offers, it demands far too much in return.

On the other hand, the deaths caused by this drug are a direct result of it being illegal. Black market varying strengths and the mixing of this powder with other things makes taking it very risky, considering the wrong combination could kill you.

That being said, it is worth noting that the number of deaths attributed to Heroin use within 1993 in the U.K. was 43. Compare this to the estimated 122 000 who will die in 1994 from tobacco use and the fact that on average one person dies every 15 minutes in the U.K. from alcohol abuse, and we can begin to see that saving lives is not the law makers main priority .

The health and well being of the user was of absolutely no concern to the British Government while they engaged in a lucrative trade with China up until the mid 1800's, trading

Heroin

Opium from it's colony India, for Chinese tea and silk. When the Chinese tried to outlaw the trading of Opium, to protect their people from addiction, the British responded by sending in gun boats to protect their huge shipments of the drug, (see your library for books on "the Opium Wars").

In more modern times up until the early 1960's, Heroin was available to addicts on prescription from your local chemist in the U.K.. It was the discontinuing of this practice which opened the door to the black market trade which exists today. Legislators were warned that this would be the result, but the warnings were ignored, as they so often are by these people.

This drug is not so much a danger to your health as it is a danger to your free will. It can take over as the most important thing in your life and have you living solely for it. You might even forget to eat most of the time. This is what causes that famous Heroin poster look, (malnutrition).

Some addicts tend to romanticise their relationship with Heroin and take an almost masochistic view of being a slave to this drug. While others try to express the dangers involved, in an attempt to warn people off the drug.

One former user I've met wrote an honest poem about it which is meant as a warning. It is reproduced here with his permission.

Lady H

So little Lady you have grown tired of Hash
LSD, Speed and Grass
A man pretending to be genuine
Sells you a bag of Heroin
Tooting it as he shows
Into your vein I soon go
So you think you have some magical knack
To try and get me off your back
Now let me tell you how it will be
You now are a slave to me
Hot shivers cold sweats your guts in a knot
One more shot and your hot
You sell all your jewellery-even your golden charms
Just to feel me again in your arm
I have your soul and your heart
You are mine till death do us part.

By M PEAKS

PROBLEMS WITH INJECTING DRUGS

These are some of the risks:

(1) Un-sterile equipment can cause infection.

(2) Sharing needles can spread disease, such as AIDS.

(3) Use new works every time to avoid infection. Taking this precaution is not expensive. Cost is about £1.40 to £1.50 for TEN syringes, (about 14P each). Most chemists sell them and will provide them with no problem. They normally come in 1/2mm 1mm 2mm and 5mm sizes. 1mm is most commonly used. 5mm is like a dart.

(4) Abscesses, Thrombosis and other conditions can result from injecting drugs in pill form never intended for this purpose.

(5) Hitting an artery instead of a vein can cause Gangrene and blood poisoning if the wound becomes infected.

(6) Injecting a drug of unknown strength can result in overdose as the substance is delivered directly into the blood stream.

OPIATES

What Is It?
A painkiller made from Opium, or more often, a synthetic form of Opium, in pills and liquid form, (as pure opium is rare in the U.K.).

Other Names:
Temgesic, Methadone, Diconal, Physeptone, Temy, Pethidine. Fire tabs, Morphine. Naps, Dipianone, Opium, DF 118's Di-Hydro-Codeine, Palfium, MTS Continuous

Where Does It Come From?
Drug firms can buy Opium legally from places such as Pakistan. NHS Pharmaceutical Companies produce synthetic opiates.

What Does It Cost?
The price of a prescription or £10 for 100mg of Methadone syrup on the black market.

Opiates

What Does It Do?
It acts on the nervous system as a painkiller. Slows down your heart rate and breathing. Creates a sense of well being, free of pain.

Can be as **ADDICTIVE** as heroin, (some say more so). It is prescribed by doctors as a legal alternative to Heroin, in the form of methadone .

As a pain killer, used during child birth or for people suffering serious pain, it can be very useful.

In the 19th century the taking of opium was quite common and it was available at your local shop without prescription. This accounts for a lot the decorations on ornate buildings of that time. The sort of concentration and lack of concern for discomfort needed to produce a gargoyle on the eaves of a building, in the pouring rain, would be provided from your friendly shop keeper in the form of Opium.

It can make you very drowsy. Using too much can put the user in a coma and even cause death.

The effects and the results of using opiates on a regular basis are much the same as that of Heroin. (see section on Heroin, What Does it Do? page 82)

This Book

PRECAUTIONS

Do not attempt to inject tablets, (the chalk will badly damage your veins).

If using injectable forms, do not share needles to prevent the spread of diseases such as AIDS.

High doses can kill.

To avoid addiction opiates should not be taken except in cases of emergency under medical supervision.

Using Methadone as a substitute for Heroin is like jumping out of the frying pan into the fire.

Taking Temgesics when you have a Heroin habit will cause you to go into withdrawals.

Legal prescription status is no measure of safety.

(see section on Serious Health Warnings page 35)

Government's Opinion

Morphine, Methadone, Pethidine Dipipanone and OPIUM are Class A (All of the above, except for Opium, are available on prescription.) Codeine is Class B and others are Class C. (see section on Drug Classes page 31)

Opiates

Author's Opinion

Another case of the government trying to have their cake and eat it too. But here we can also see that they have an almost fanatical belief in their own powers. They seem to believe that their making something CLASS A *actually makes it bad,* while what they don't touch with their legislative wand *remains good.*

So Heroin is banned while it's synthetic forms can be freely prescribed by doctors.

The result of this wild value judgment is that a person wishing to stop taking Heroin can be prescribed Methadone, which is every bit as addictive. This is to save the user from the withdrawals of Heroin, but the withdrawals from Methadone are known to be much worse and last much longer!

The only consolation the user can have while suffering all this extra time is that at least now their suffering is legal.

The use of pain killers by people in desperate pain makes sense. If one becomes addicted under those circumstances, they might well consider this a fair price to pay. But to a healthy person this drug demands far too much in return to be sensible.

BARBITURATES

What Is It?
A sedative hypnotic drug which comes in a powdered form, sold in coloured capsules.

Other Names:
Sodium Amytal, Seconal, Tuinal, Barbs, Downers, Blues, Reds, Sekkies.

Where Does It Come From?
These are produced by pharmaceutical companies and prescribed by doctors. Also available on the black market.

What Does It Cost?
The price of a prescription or about £1.00 per capsule on the streets.

Barbiturates

What Does It Do?

This drug was originally produced to induce sleep, but it is rarely prescribed for this purpose any more, due to the fact that many people during the 70's died from Barbiturate poisoning, (approximately 2000 per year).

The effect is not all that enjoyable. Users experience a sense of oblivion, blank and dark. The result is an escape from reality to nowhere.

Users can become nervous and irritable.

Barbiturates are **VERY ADDICTIVE** and the withdrawals very dangerous and sometimes fatal, (while no-body dies from opiate withdrawals, it can happen on Barbiturates).

These are generally popular with people who feel they have little to live for and simply wish to blot everything out, one hairs breath short of committing suicide. It's sad for those who die in the process never to give their lives a second chance.

PRECAUTIONS

Under the influence it is easy to forget how much you have taken, resulting in overdose.

These are **VERY ADDICTIVE** and not to be underestimated.

Mixing with alcohol can be fatal.

These can slow down your system and your heartbeat to the point where everything stops and you die.

Injecting creates a greater risk of overdose.

If one is unfortunate enough to become addicted to Barbiturates, attempting to come off them should only be done under medical supervision, preferably as a hospital in-patient.

Government's Opinion
Legal with prescription.

By all accounts this drug is much more dangerous than Heroin, yet it's manufacturers and main distributors have never been persecuted or put in prison. This is another example of society's double standards.

Author's Opinion
These are not as common as they used to be, which is a good thing. Barbiturates have little to recommend them. Their use as an act of desperation can spoil the users chances of ever seeing the bright side again.

NEEDLE ADDICTION

Addiction can be more than just the need for a drug and often takes the form of a ritual which some users find as exciting as taking the drug itself.

What users call "setting up your next hit" usually involves the same routine each time, with each step carefully and religiously carried out in the same order. This can start from the moment the user sets out to acquire the drug and end when the drug reaches their blood stream.

The actual process of injecting can have an addictive quality all it's own. Users will flush blood back into the syringe before removing the needle and re-inject the blood to recreate the sensation.

Some users also have a fascination with the sound of the needle piercing the skin which is referred to as "*popping in*". This they claim can be heard in their heads as well as through their ears.

Needle addiction and an attraction to the sensations of the preparation ritual can make it much more difficult for a user when they try to stop. While this might sound unbelievable to a non user, it is a very serious problem which many addicts cannot find the will power to overcome.

HOW MUCH ! ? !

Producing a kilo of Tobacco is not much different from producing a kilo of Marijuana, yet ounce for ounce, Marijuana can cost 40 times as much as tobacco.

The effort and knowledge needed to produce a kilo of Cocaine is on a par with that needed to produce a kilo of instant Coffee, (both produced in the same country). Yet gram for gram Cocaine can cost 5000 times as much as instant Coffee.

The prices paid by the individual user (which we include in the What Does It Cost ? sections) is greatly inflated from the original price by what smugglers and dealers add on to compensate them for the risk they take. At the source, these things are not really very expensive at all. It is society which boost the value of these things by giving them an illegal certificate.

Mr Big!

This Book

On the news you will often hear how the police claim they have seized millions of pounds worth of drugs. In most cases they are lying, by any calculation you care to make.

These huge figures make good headlines, but they bear no relationship to reality or the persons arrested. The 25 kilos of cannabis seized, worth over a million pounds on the news, was probably bought from some peasant farmer for about £2500 .

Even if the whole lot could be broken down into 14,400 bits the size of an eraser, to be sold individually at *extortionate* prices, it is not likely that our smuggler making the headlines would undertake to do all this *all on his own*. Yet when the figures are quoted people are led to believe it's all down to one person.

What they always neglect to mention is that it is the laws against drugs which make smuggling profitable, and nothing else. What they claim to be fighting is actually a thing of their own creation.

ALCOHOL

What Is It?
It is a volatile colourless
inflammable liquid which
is the intoxicating element
in wine, beer and spirits. It
can also be used as fuel
and as a solvent.

Other Names:
The Brand names of wine beer and spirits, booze, vino, a
pint, a tipple. a shot or a wee dram, hooch.

Where Does It Come From ?
Yeast, added to organic material breaks it down changing
the sugar to ethyl alcohol, (a process called fermentation).
Alcohol is produced in the form of beer, wine and spirits
by drink companies round the world (from grapes, hops,
grain etc,) and sold in pubs and off licenses. It can also be
legally made in the home, with brewing kits or a bucket,
some fruit, sugar and yeast, given time to ferment, (instructions are easily available from your library and local book
stores).

What Does It Cost?
The price can vary greatly according to the variety of product from about 40p for a can of beer to hundreds of pounds
for a bottle of rare wine.

Alcohol

What Does It Do?

Technically it is a depressant. In actual fact it helps people to drop their inhibitions. It's effects vary with the amount taken.

A drink or two can make a person jolly and more talkative.

A few more drinks can help a person forget their worries also making walking unsteady. Even more can cause wild mood swings bringing the user to tears or inspiring them to be violent. They might also experience double vision. Add more to that and the user can loose control, doing things that he or she will not remember doing the next day. Take even more and the user can pass out.

Drinking too much *(being drunk)* can cause the user to vomit uncontrollably sometimes long after the contents of their stomach has been spewed out, which is referred to as the *dry heaves*.

The next day is accompanied by headaches and an ill feeling with dehydration, known as a hangover.

It is **POSSIBLE TO OVERDOSE** on this drug, (which happens often in the U.K).

While this drug can put you in the mood for lovemaking, it does nothing to improve your performance and can even hamper it.

This Book

There is more violence caused by alcohol than by any other substance known to man, and as a result alcohol is responsible for a large portion of violent crime.

This drug can be **ADDICTIVE** with constant use. Alcohol addicts are called *alcoholics*. An organisation called Alcoholics Anonymous has been set up to help alcoholics to stop drinking and to live normal lives again.

Alcohol can seriously damage the nervous system. It is the only readily available intoxicant which can do so. On average one person dies every 15 minutes in the U.K from alcohol abuse, (365 days a year, including Christmas and New Year).

But: there are millions of people who drink only occasionally, do not become alcoholics and do not suffer from alcohol use, (estimated at over 40 million users in the U.K.).

Then there is Absinthe, an anise-flavoured liqueur distilled with oil of wormwood, a leafy herb, also containing flavourful herbs like hyssop, lemon balm and angelica, said to have been enjoyed by Vincent Van Gogh, Ernest Hemingway, Paul Verlaine and Oscar Wilde. It has been banned in the USA since 1912 but can still be bought in some off licenses in Britain, Spain and reportedly in Denmark and Portugal as well.

Alcohol

PRECAUTIONS

All the problems related to alcohol are a result of drinking *too much*. To avoid problems, don't over do it.

To avoid Addiction, do not use on a daily basis.

Mixing with Opiates can be fatal slowing the system to a halt.

Should be avoided by anyone who has experienced liver damage.

Mixing drinks, like beer and wine or wine and spirits etc. can make you ill even in small amounts.

Drinking does not mean you need to get drunk. Never keep knocking back drinks as a dare. People have died doing this. **Overdose is possible.**

Drinking milk or having a meal before a few drinks will coat the stomach and slow down the absorption of alcohol into your system. But if you overdo it, remember you'll have that much more to vomit.

Don't forget that spirits are much stronger than beer and wine and can affect you greatly with small doses.

Being drunk makes a person more accident prone, e.g. losing their balance and injuring themselves in a fall.

This Book

Prolonged drinking can cause liver damage, (particularly Cirrhosis of the liver), various cancers, Pancreatitis and ulcers. It can lead to heart problems and even brain damage.

Some young people think that *getting drunk* makes them more grown up, but in reality it's only immature people who get drunk. It's far more grown up to know when to stop.

(see Serious Health Warnings page 35)

Government's Opinion
Legal, can be sold by licensed vendors to anyone over 18 years of age.

Drinking and Driving is illegal if over the limit, which can result in losing your licence and a £200 fine and even 6 months in prison, (not to mention the loss of your life and others you might crash into).

Limits are set on times of the day when alcohol can be legally sold.

Author's Opinion
They tried to ban alcohol in the United States with no success. In countries which call themselves *Christian*, it is hardly likely they will proclaim Christ's first miracle (turning water into wine) illegal.

Alcohol

This is a drug that the people who make the laws like to take themselves, so they are willing to overlook the irresponsible minority who harm themselves with over use.

The law which allows the running of pubs and off licenses to sell alcohol makes it an acceptable and respectable thing in society. "Yes, it does destroy some people's lives, and some people do die from using it", they say, "but why allow a small percentage to spoil everyone else's fun ?"

People who have suffered or are suffering as the result of alcohol abuse, by them or someone close to them, might wish booze was banned; but banning things does not stop them from being used, and if alcohol had been banned, they might be suffering from it just the same. All things considered, the government's view on this one is reasonable. (*Even a broken clock is right twice a day.*)

Proper production controls insure the quality of what is sold. The privilege is extended in a mature way, allowing grown up people to decide for themselves, and in the majority of cases, the privilege is not abused.

There will always be people who will over do it. This minority should never be used as an excuse for preventing the rest of the people from sensibly enjoying themselves. The group who over do it and harm themselves and others will only be diminished by *honest education* and not *hypocritical legislation.*

Show me the way to go home. . .

SOLVENTS

What Is It?
The fumes from cleaning agents, glue, nail polish, nail polish remover, petrol, anti-freeze, correction fluids, aerosol products, some dyes, lighter fluid, and fire extinguishers, which are inhaled from a cloth or a bag.

Other Names:
The brand names of the above.

Where Does It Come From?
Produced by companies and sold in shops.

What Does It Cost?
Widely available at low cost. Varies according to the product.

Solvents

What Does It Do?
Has been described as being the lowest of the lowest kind of buzz.

As the user breathes in toxic fumes from the above mentioned products, the brain is starved of oxygen. Feeling itself being poisoned, it gets confused and starts to retreat into a dream state. With some users this panic dream state combines with reality to cause hallucinations. Others feel dizzy, light headed and experience blackouts.

Loss of consciousness while breathing in solvents can result in the person choking on their own vomit, not being aware enough to spit it out.

The effects of sniffing can last from 15 to 45 minutes. An ill feeling with drowsiness can follow, lasting into the next day.

People who partake in solvents on a regular basis find their thinking process goes dull.

There have been cases of users dying from heart failure and suffocation.

This drug can be **VERY ADDICTIVE, with constant use** especially butane and certain glues.

PRECAUTIONS
Assuming you really do wish to experience the effects of toxic poisoning:

Be aware of how flammable these things are, and don't light a flame near them, ie: No Smoking.

Have someone with you, not partaking, who will agree in advance to help keep clear your air passages should you black out and vomit.

Never squirt aerosol gasses directly into the mouth. This can cause air passages to freeze and result in suffocation.

Long term use can cause lasting kidney and liver damage.

Never put your head inside a bag or container to sniff solvents. People have died this way from suffocation.

There is no precaution you can take to avoid possible heart failure, apart from leaving solvents alone.

(see section on Serious Health Warnings page 35)

Solvents

IN AN EMERGENCY

If you come across someone being ill or passed out from use of solvents:

(1) Remove the solvent from their face.

(2) Loosen clothing, (theirs, not yours).

(3) Check to see if they are breathing, if not, seek out someone to administer CPR, if you are not trained to do so yourself.

(4) Provide ventilation by opening windows or doors.

(5) If person remains unconscious CALL AN AMBU-LANCE!

(6) Lie the person down on their stomach with head turned to one side, (the recovery position).

(7) Be sure air passages are clear of any vomit.

(8) Stay with them until they recover or the ambulance arrives.

This Book

Government's Opinion
Completely legal, except it is illegal to supply these substances to people under the age of 18, if the shopkeeper *knows* they intend to sniff them.

ie: If the shopkeeper is a mind reader, or a person under 18 asks for *some glue to sniff,* then selling some to them would be an offense. Presumably a person over 18 years of age can inquire and purchase solvents for sniffing with no problem at all.

Author's Opinion
Within Great Britain 149 people died as the result of solvent abuse in 1990. Most of them were children. Within that same time, there were no reported deaths from the use of Cannabis.

Solvents exist within products which are otherwise useful, and it would not be realistic to try and stop their production.

As far back as history records, people have experimented with things which can alter their consciousness. Curiosity is a natural and healthy thing in young people.

Perhaps if Cannabis had been as inexpensive and easy to obtain as the Solvents were for those 149 people who died, many of them might still be alive today?

AMYL NITRATE

What Is It?
A liquid produced by pharmaceutical
companies for recreational use. The
vapour is inhaled through the nose.

Other Names:
Amyl, Poppers

Where Does It Come From?
It can be Amyl Nitrate or Butyl
Nitrate produced by pharmaceutical labs.

Amyl Nitrate - from NHS sources. Butyl Nitrate - from sex
shops and head shops for recreational use.

What Does It Cost?
£5 to £8 per bottle.

What Does It Do?
It reduces blood pressure by enlarging blood vessels, which
causes the heart to pump more quickly. The term "rush"
describes the feeling of blood rushing through the body
more quickly than usual. This sensation can be enjoyable.
Some people get dizzy and black out using this drug.
Others claim it heightens sexual arousal.

Weight lifters sometimes have a sniff before a lift.

Amyl Nitrate

In the mid 1800's it was used as a treatment for angina, because of it's ability to expand blood vessels. This use has been discontinued.

PRECAUTIONS
Those with low blood pressure or heart problems should avoid this drug.

Do not swallow or inject.

This can make your nose sore creating a burning sensation when you reach the end of a bottle.

(see section on Serious Health Warnings page 35).

Government's Opinion
Completely Legal.

Author's Opinion
No big deal, but don't make a habit of it. The legal status of this drug is out of character with the government's attitude towards recreational drugs. Makes one really wonder what guidelines our present legislators use to decide what should or should not be banned.

This drug is popular with the gay community. It is also produced by well established pharmaceutical companies. Is there possibly a clue here as to why this drug remains unrestricted by M.Ps?

PSYCHEDELIC DRUGS

Preparing a space for a Trip.

Psychedelic is defined in the Concise Oxford Dictionary as: expanding the minds awareness etc., especially through the use of hallucinogenic drugs.

Among the definitions for Trip we find: a journey or excursion, especially for pleasure, and a hallucinatory experience caused by a drug.

In the next section we will be taking a look at some *psychedelic drugs*.

Before we start to discuss each in detail, there are a few things which can be said about these drugs in general, (especially the l*egal one's* you might be tempted to try).

Psychedelic Drugs

There is a clue in the definition above as to what makes these drugs different from other drugs, *"expanding the minds awareness"*. These drugs rather than working on the body actually work on the mind.

Normally the mind is put in touch with the real world through the five senses, touch, hearing, smell, sight and taste. It not only takes in this information from the senses but also decides what is important and what is not.

To a hungry man the smell of food will be much more important than it would be to a man who has just eaten.

Of all the information the mind receives, only a small part is actually of any use for survival. What the mind attempts to do is use what it needs and filter out the rest. Hence, our hungry man would make a B-line for the food he smells, paying no attention to the scent of many flowers he might pass on the way.

To stay and sniff the flowers might mean he would miss the food he needs to survive, so the mind filters out the scent of the flowers.

Another example which might sound familiar is that of a family living in the flight path of an airport. After some time, the sound of the aircraft passing overhead blends into the background for them, whereas a much softer tap on their door would make them stop to answer it.

This Book

While going through everyday life these filters are working constantly to show us what we need and filtering out the rest. What happens when you take a psychedelic drug is that the filters are temporarily left wide open.

The colour and scent of the flowers you might have passed and ignored yesterday suddenly are too bright and aromatic to ignore now. The blue sky, which might not merit more than a glance on a busy day, now is so blue you might spend hours admiring it.

With the filters open the mind is now flooded with all sorts of information it's never had to deal with all at once before.

Plus: At night you dream. You imagine things in your mind to be real. During the day the dream filter is closed tight so you can cope with everyday life, shutting out dream images.

Take a psychedelic drug and for a period of time known as *peaking*, (lasting 3 to 5 hours), the dream filter is thrown open, and dreamy things can start to appear right along side real life. This is called a hallucination. You might see colourful mists floating around the room you are sitting in for instance.

The mind, receiving signals from the real world and your dream world simultaneously, with no filters, simply combines what it is being sent into one picture, like two projectors projecting onto the same screen.

Psychedelic Drugs

Within your mind there is a great *sense of order* you normally know very little about. Your mind keeps your heart beating at a steady rate, keeps you breathing, and your temperature constant. The division of cells and the digestion of food goes on within you without your needing to know about it. The necessary things continue to happen, day and night, but awareness of their activity is filtered out so you are not distracted or preoccupied by it.

Take a psychedelic drug and you might become aware of the flow of things within you, if that filter opens up. You might become aware that all you've ever eaten has been alive before, and you might see your place in the Circle of Life. Such claims have been made for psychedelic drugs, hence, even in the dictionary the term "*expanding the mind's awareness*" occurs.

Being flooded with all this information all at once can be an amazing experience, but to really enjoy it, one needs to prepare themselves for it.

Next we will have a description of what a wise tripper might do to prepare for a trip and explain why. *While you might never intend to try a psychedelic drug, you might find it interesting to hear what preparing for a safe trip entails.*

If the mind expanding drug can bring out all the detail in a flower, to make it interesting enough to look at for hours, it can also amplify things which might cause you distress, and make them all the more distressing. With the mind's filters open there is nothing to protect you from what you might see, so a clever tripper decides what to look at and experience during a trip IN ADVANCE!

What a psychedelic drug can do to the senses, it can also do to the emotions, so one doesn't really want to take this when they are sad or down, because without the filters help, they will experience their sadness in detail beyond what they would ever wish for.

When something distressing happens to us, normally the filters block out most of it and leave us to deal with the essence of the thing. Open the filters and the distress will hit you full whack, (this is what we call a Bad Trip).

Often a kind word from someone not on the drug, to point out to the tripper that they are exaggerating or hallucinating, and that there is no real problem, is all they need to set them on a happy coarse again from a potentially bad trip. It is therefore a very good idea to have someone, not partaking, they can trust, agree to act as their baby sitter while they trip. Someone who has previous experience of the drug can be extra helpful playing this part.

What follows is a fact which every user should know to avoid many problems .

Psychedelic Drugs

A psychedelic drug acts like a *huge magnifying glass on life*. The clever tripper does not leave what might be magnified to chance. They plan the trip, prepare the space, invite the right friends, select their favourite music, gather up interesting things to look at and explore, have interesting things to eat like bowls of fruit and boxes of chocolate ready. They make a real event of the day. They would wait until they were in a happy mood already, so as to experience *that* mood in an amplified way, with a good friend to keep an eye on them. In this environment this tripper is given every chance of an enjoyable time, (A good Trip). An unusual pleasant special time.

Psychedelic drugs are not addictive drugs and not the kind of thing you want to take daily. Unlike drugs which demand that you take more and more, day after day, most psychedelic drugs do not work very well taken two days in a row. By design these drugs are very much a special event thing. The many North and South American Indians tribes who placed great importance on psychedelic experiences, to put them in tune with nature, might use them for ceremonies to greet each new season. This moderate approach is a good one when we considering the nature of these drugs. **Once per season gives plenty of time to recover, and to put into practice what one might learn.**

In preparing their space there are two other things a clever tripper would do.

This Book

One: On the day they intend to trip, they would make themselves be completely free of any other responsibilities. They would treat the day like they've gone away, even if tripping in their own home. They might even put a *Do Not Disturb* sign on their door and disconnect their phone if they have one. Let people they'd rather not see that day know that they'll be busy.

And two: They would arrange it so they had the next day off with absolutely nothing to do but relax. A person doesn't really want to be dealing with complicated things while their mind is adjusting back to normal, after being overwhelmed by sights, sounds, feelings, and ideas coming at them on overdrive. This is a time when they need to be able to sit back and relax with no other concerns in the world. It's a treat and a break.

All good things in this world need preparation, a good meal, a musical concert a sculptured garden. To be truly enjoyable, a trip on a mind expanding drug needs loving preparation too.

It is called a trip after all, and before you go on any trip you plan the route and pack your bags with all you'll need to make it enjoyable and exciting. Most of the getting there safely is in getting ready properly.

Wise trippers always lovingly plan their trips.

THE EASY WAY OUT

Times vary a little from one psychedelic drug to another, but on average the experience starts between 45 minutes and an hour from consuming the drug. The effect increases over the next 2 or 3 hours reaching a peak which can last from 1 to 3 hours (5 hours if it's really strong), then the user spends the next 6 to 8 hours coming down to reality again, at which time they will be able to sleep.

Say they have made all their preparations well, but for some unusual reason they hadn't expected, they are not enjoying the experience. They are committed to remain tripping for the next 12 hours or so, right ?

Wrong ! Not if they use this little trick I'll explain. Here is what they do in advance of the trip.

They go to their doctor and explain that they would like something to help them sleep. They only want this for *a maximum of two nights* to set them right, and want no more than that because they know these things can be habit forming if taken for any length of time. They might say they have a couple of really eventful days coming up that they want to be sure they are well rested for, (true).

Their request being for only two days is very reasonable and providing they haven't asked for these sort of things constantly before, their doctor should grant it. If he or she does not, they **should see another doctor.** This is important! Having used their persistence and charm they can have the prescription filled. Now they have two days supply of sleeping pills. What on earth are these for, you might be wondering, if you haven't worked it out already?

One day's worth of sleeping pills will usually overcome the effects of a psychedelic drug and send you off peacefully to sleep. Two days worth should definitely do the trick and that much won't harm a healthy person. *(If they have any doubts about their health this would be a good time to have a checkup.)*

If they have real problems with seeing their doctor, they can always go to their local chemist's and buy a bottle of *Night Nurse*. Drinking half the bottle will work really well putting them to sleep with no bad side effects.

Psychedelic Drugs

When planning their trip, wise trippers make sure there is a place nearby where they can just comfortably go to sleep if they feel like it. It can be their bedroom, a tent, even the back seat of a car with blankets and pillows ready. If at any time during their trip they feel like they'd like to stop, they go to their resting place and take the pills, (or half a bottle of *Night Nurse*).

Within about 30 minutes they'll be relaxing off to sleep and when they wake up the intense part of their trip will be over and they will feel fine.

For many people, just the idea that it is possible to stop the trip at any time is a comfort which makes the whole trip more enjoyable.

Oh, and one more thing, should their doctor be generous and supply them with more than the 2 days worth they ask for, they would be wise to keep 2 days worth and *flush the rest down the toilet*. That way there is no chance of them taking too many by mistake.

If they are sensible, they won't want to trip all that often, and given a reasonable space of time, say two or three months or so, their doctor won't mind providing them with another couple of days worth of pills if they ask.

Now you've got the idea of how important it is for our wise tripper to lovingly prepare their space before tripping and provide an *easy way out* should they feel it's needed, we are ready to take a look at some psychedelic drugs.

There might be some who will say that by explaining to you how to make a psychedelic trip safe and enjoyable as possible, that I am encouraging you to break the law. These people will not be aware that there are some excellent psychedelic drugs available which are *completely legal* to take. We will look at one in our next chapter. And besides, laws are changing all the time. There's no telling what might be legal tomorrow. No harm in being ready, is there? And for those of you just satisfying your curiosity, there's no harm in that either.

MAGIC MUSHROOMS

What Is It?
Types of psychoactive mushrooms which are eaten, raw

Other Names:
Psilocybin mushrooms, Liberty cap, White rockets (owing to them being white and rocket shaped) and many more.

Where Does It Come From?
Grows wild in damp fields, (from Sept. to Nov. in the U.K.).

What Does It Cost?
Free for the picking. Some are re-sold in bags of 20 to 40 mushrooms for between £5 and £10 a bag.

What Does It Do?
Small amounts from 5 to 20 or so will bring on a sense of well being, good humour, laughing fits and general jollity lasting a few hours.

Magic Mushrooms

Larger amounts from 20 to 50 or so can have a very definite psychedelic effect on the user, lasting between 8 and 12 hours, (see section on Psychedelic Drugs, page 117). The trip will start about 45 minutes to an hour after consuming the mushrooms.

They vary from other mind expanding drugs in that the way this drug allows your senses to be flooded leaves little room for the user to consider much else. As a result the user is less likely to concentrate on anything depressing, which makes bad trips uncommon.

A strong dose will produce a cascade of colours all around you which can continue even if you close your eyes. Taken in a natural setting, in a garden, a park, by the sea, or in a forest, mushrooms will bring out your surroundings and give a fairy tale edge to them, enhancing the colours and your relationship to the plants.

A user might be fascinated by how the veins in their hands have a similar pattern to the branches of a tree, for instance. One might even claim they can sense the sap flowing in the trees and feel a oneness with this and the way their own blood is flowing through their body.

As with all mind expanding drugs, small things may take on a huge importance to the user, and they might sit examining a leaf or a piece of glass for hours.

Although, on a strong trip, you will see colours and patterns projected by your mind, which are not there to the non user, you are not likely to lose sight of where you actually are. For instance your garden might be full of colourful mists in the air, but you will still know it's your garden. Sometimes hallucinations can be shared by a group tripping together.

The next day your mind might feel tired from the overload, but you will soon return to normal.

Magic mushrooms have been used for thousands of years by people of ancient times seeking spiritual experiences.

PRECAUTIONS
The section on Psychedelic Drugs (page 117) has some good suggestions on how to prepare your space for a trip. All these apply well here.

To remind us: First time trippers should have someone *not tripping* with them to keep them safe during this new experience.

Remember our Superman rule - if you feel like trying to fly, do it always FROM THE GROUND UP !

Take small amounts to get the feel of it first, (5 to 10 mushrooms).

Be in a good mood *"before"* you start.

Magic Mushrooms

If you have any history of mental illness or doubts about your mental health, this drug is not for you.

When picking mushrooms, take great care as eating the wrong variety could be fatal. Go to your local library or book shop and consult a guide such as Collins Guide to Mushrooms. Bring the book or photo copies of the mushroom you intend to pick with you. (The Liberty Cap is the most common, but you will find references to other hallucinogenic, psychoactive mushrooms, if you look.) Pick only mushrooms which fit *perfectly* the book's description, and IF IN DOUBT, LEAVE IT.

If you are acquiring mushrooms from someone else, and you are unsure of the variety from their dried state, you could always use the This Book Powder Poison Test, (see section on Powders page 59) to be sure, but be aware that in this state these are counted as Class A.

Take the *Licence to Trip Test,* which you will find coming up on page 147. Make sure you understand each question and can pass without cheating.

(see Serious Warnings page 35)

Government's Opinion
It is completely legal for you to go out picking Magic Mushrooms. It is also legal for you to eat the Magic Mushrooms you have picked in order to trip.

This Book

The law says you are not allowed to process the mushrooms in any way which includes drying them. The element within the mushrooms which make them psychoactive *(trippy)* is called Psilocybin which is rated a Class A drug. See the next chapter dedicated to Psilocybin.

Author's Opinion
These mushrooms are so common in some parts of the country, if having them on your land was illegal, a huge number of influential land owners including members of the Royal Family could be placed under arrest.

Our lengthy discussion on psychedelic drugs is not included just to fill pages. Preparation and attitude are vital when experiencing mind expanding drugs. The legal status of Magic Mushrooms provides the opportunity for anyone interested in having a genuine mind expanding psychedelic experience to do so, without the risk of imprisonment.

The trouble you'll need to go through researching the varieties in books, finding where they grow, going out in the early morning to pick them, and carefully preparing your space to take them, will provide a real adventure that you are not likely to want to repeat too often, which is how nature intended it, and how it should be.

Magic Mushrooms can have a very powerful effect, and should be treated with respect, as they were treated by people of ancient times, who used them only on special occasions.

I don't care whose garden it's in,
as soon as it's dry we're nicking them!

PSILOCYBIN

What Is It?
A hallucinogenic alkaloid found in some mushrooms. This
is the element in the mushroom which makes them psychoactive *(trippy)*, in powder or capsule form.

Other Names :
Essence of magic mushrooms, Mushroom pills, Silly Side
Bin.

What Does It Cost?
From £5 to £10 per capsule.

What Does It Do?
This is a strong psychedelic drug, one dose producing more
or less the same effect as eating *40 or more Magic
Mushrooms,* without having to pick them.

Since this is actually the active ingredient in Magic
Mushrooms, all the things said in the previous chapter
about mushrooms apply here, except for the instructions on
picking, (if you haven't already, you should read the previous chapter, starting on page 129).

Psilocybin

PRECAUTIONS
All the general information concerning Psychedelic Drugs applies here, (re - read if necessary from page 117).

Before taking, be sure you can easily pass the *Licence to Trip Test*, (see page 147 to start).

The powder form this comes in makes it difficult to know for sure what you are getting, (see Powders page 59).

(see section on Serious Health Warnings, page 35)

Government's Opinion
Illegal Class A (see section on Drug Classes, page 31)

This also includes dried or processed mushrooms.

Author's Opinion
The information on this drug you will have noticed is practically identical to that for Magic Mushrooms. That is because this is *the same substance* contained in the mushrooms which gives them their psychedelic *(trippy)* effect.

So why have a separate section for it you may ask? Because in this form a formerly legal substance *magically* becomes Class A illegal when it is removed from it's source or dried, and of this you should be aware.

Now here we have an example of some very weird logic indeed. The government's usual excuse for banning a thing is that they say it's not good for us. But here we see that their objection is not against us *taking* the drug but against our *processing* it.

Could it be our leaders have left the taking of Magic Mushroom legal because *they* enjoy taking them? I doubt that very much. The thoughts they have and express are not the sort inspired by psychedelic drugs.

So that leaves us with two options.

The reason they have banned the substance *in* the mushroom but not the substance *with* the mushroom can either be because they are completely incompetent *, or maybe they are concerned about some untaxed money being made.

This is a fine example of the people ruling us making absolutely no sense at all.

there is a lot of evidence for this

FROM THE GROUND UP!

LSD

What Is It?
A chemical whose full name is Lysergic acid diethylamide, which is ingested in liquid, pill, blotter and gelatin square form (rarely injected).

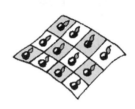

Other Names:
Acid, Tabs, Trips, A, Micro dots, window panes or by numerous designs - Rockets, Smilies, Dragons. Stars, many cartoon characters, plus Purple Oms, Strawberries, Floyds Penguin, and Penny to name but a few.

Where Does It Come From?
It is synthesised from mould. Was accidentally discovered by a Swiss chemist named Albert Hoffman who mistakingly ingested some while doing animal tests and had the first trip in April 1943. (God's answer to the Second World War?)

What Does It Cost?
£2 to £5 per dose.

LSD

What Does It Do?
This drug will produce a complete psychedelic experience (a trip) which can last up to 12 hours, (see section on Psychedelic Drugs page 117 if you haven't already).

The effects begin within an hour of eating it, continuing to increase in intensity for a couple of hours, staying at the peak from 1 to 3 hours, (5 if it's really strong) with several hours to follow coming down to normal again before you can sleep.

Most common hallucinations are colours floating in the air, sometimes referred to as *Scotch Mist*. Though you might see colourful things which are not there, you are not likely to forget where you are on this drug.

Most of the problems ascribed to this drug, like people losing control and having bad trips, were a result of the doses being extra strong in the 60's. In those days one hit could contain 12 to 15 times as much LSD as the average dose contains in the 90's! (LSD did not start out being very expensive in the 60's. As time moved on into the 70's and the 80's, street dealers resisted any price rise, saying the buyers would not pay more. To counteract this, the producers kept the price stable, but reduced the strength of each hit.)

Taken in huge doses common in the 60's this drug can really make you sit back, but with doses common in the

90's people can go dancing, have fun and not be hampered by the drug, *once accustomed to it.*

In the 60's there were stories circulating claiming that LSD could cause chromosome damage and result in the birth of deformed children. When these affected children failed to arrive, researchers were forced to admit that these stories were in fact propaganda produced by the United States government, and had no basis in experimentation or fact.

During this time the idea of *Flash Backs* was introduced. According to some documentaries, a user might find himself tripping again months after the initial trip was over. A crane operator suddenly finds himself tripping and his wrecking ball hits the wrong house, is an image I seem to recall. In truth, a user might be reminded of how a trip felt and re-experience the feeling for a fleeting moment, much like recalling the atmosphere of a special place from hearing a song you first heard there, but you are not likely to lose control of your crane over this.

This drug is typical of psychedelic drugs which is why I've referred you back to that section. It will amplify whatever you are experiencing at the time. Colours can become very bright and deep in things around you. It's like being in a technicolour movie, with added colours floating in the air.

It will let you view yourself and your situation in a way you have never observed before. Whatever you examine or think about will take on a huge importance.

LSD

Where mushrooms have a very overwhelming effect that sort of wraps you up, this drug has a real edge to it. You will be able to go deeply into depressing things if that is what you happen to explore, so precautions to avoid this are essential (see section starting on page 117).

One might well feel the blood flowing through their veins and energy all around them, but very few full blown hallucinations are reported. A normal light might seem to glow all different colours, but one is unlikely to see things that seem solid which are not actually there.

Where mushrooms could be described as a gentle magic carpet journey, LSD can be like a roller coaster ride. If you go with the flow you'll enjoy it, but if you try to fight it, you'll fall off. This is not a drug for the faint hearted. It can put you through some amazing changes in a short period of time providing a really thrilling ride of emotions and images.

If the room starts to swim with colour and the walls start to breath in and out don't panic, enjoy it, you are just tripping. All will be normal tomorrow.

On your first trip it is best to remain in a controlled comfortable environment, as our section on Psychedelic Drugs describes. But once you become familiar with how it works, on future trips, you will be able to venture out a bit if you wish.

You will need to wait a while before tripping again because Acid does not work very well two days in a row. It works by setting loose adrenaline type substances within your mind, but your mind has only so much in stock and once that is spent it can take several weeks to build up a full new stock again. It acts as a catalyst, that is to say it sets in motion what is already there.

In a crowd, such as at a rave, the oneness of humankind will become clear as the whole mass of people dance as one.

Music can sound like it's never sounded before and everyday things can take on a special significance to the user.

Taken outside, the beauty of nature will assault you from all sides. The colour of flowers will be brighter, their scent stronger and the sky bluer than ever. If it starts to rain, you might see it as life falling from the sky, (which it is).

People on LSD tend to see themselves as *part of* nature when tripping outside. You are not a person walking in the park, you are part of the park while you're there and the trees and grass make you feel welcome.

Some users enjoy laying back with their eyes closed, experiencing an exaggerated sort of daydream.

LSD

It can make you very sentimental, with your loved ones and your friends taking on an intense loving meaning. A feeling of warmth and Love for the Earth, the Universe, Life, and all of Humankind is common. This is the drug which inspired the 60's Peace Movement which lives on in organisations such as Green Peace today.

PRECAUTIONS

If you have a history of mental illness, this drug is not for you.

Re-read the section on Psychedelic Drugs starting page 117 and take the time to make your preparations carefully.

To Remind you: Be prepared for a complete experience and have your place ready to use your *Easy Way Out,* should you feel it's too much for you, (review *The Easy Way Out* page 124).

Have a good friend agree to *baby sit* you for the duration. If they have no experience with psychedelics, have them read from page 117 to page 127 in This Book. They can remind you, should you feel like trying to fly, to try only FROM THE GROUND UP.

Cut the hit in two and take only half the first time.

While this can be fun at a rave for an experienced user, this is not the ideal place to have your first trip.

This Book

Do not take this drug to overcome depression. If you are depressed this drug will make you more depressed. Be in a good mood to start with.

Dwelling on any guilt you may have from events in the past, or fear you might have for the future can produce a Bad Trip. If this concerns you, make a point of reading THAT BOOK The Things They Don't Teach You In School, before tripping, (see page 323 in This Book).

Do the *Licence To Trip Test* which you will find in the Author's Opinion section of this chapter as you read on (page 147). Make sure you understand each question and can pass without cheating.

(see section on Serious Health Warnings page 35)

Government's Opinion
Illegal in the U.K. since 1966 CLASS A (See Section on Drug Classes page 31)

Author's Opinion
LSD was made illegal as a reaction by the system to the 60's Peace Movement.

When things are going well in your mind and when you are at a comfortable time in your life both mentally and physically is the *only* time to take LSD. Those who follow this rule will avoid bad trips.

LSD

The trip can be seen like a journey to a mountain top. From there the view is good but to really take advantage of what we see, we need to climb down into the villages and valleys to really live. No matter how beautiful the view, it only becomes of any real use when you reach home again.

They use the fact that some people have had bad trips and fallen out of high buildings as a reason to ban LSD. But they don't ban cars because a few people crash and die in them, sad as it is. Why not? They put it down to bad driving.

If a person jumps out of a building, thinking they can fly on LSD, I put that down to bad instructions. Everyone knows the only *real* way to try and fly is from the ground up, and nothing else counts as real flight.

If you tell me you can fly I say show me from the ground up! I've tried this myself running down a steep hill and it's amazing how far you fly from one step to the other. A fantasy tried, no harm done, and nobody died.

To take LSD or other psychedelics you should be required to sit a test and be issued with a licence if you pass. You don't let untrained people into cars onto the open road to try their luck. No more should you allow people who have no idea what psychedelics are to trip.

This Book

This is what I imagine the test might look like.

THE ACID TEST

For a Licence to Trip on Psychedelics
A futuristic pretend Rainbow Land Test

Valid for tripping on: Magic Mushrooms LSD*
Mescaline* Psilocybin *

Not valid for DMT, Toad or STP unless you have *first hand experience* of one or more of the above.

The questions which follow test the knowledge needed to make tripping as safe as possible. All answers can be found in This Book.

Upon going to print, the law in the U.K. prohibits the use of LSD Mescaline and Psilocybin. This test is therefore only valid for tripping on Mushrooms and Toad today, and for tripping on LSD Mescaline and Psilocybin in the future should they become legal.

LSD

PART ONE

A) Have you had a recent physical checkup from your doctor?

YES/NO

If you answered NO, read the section on Serious Health Warnings and arrange a checkup.

B) If you answered YES, did your doctor discover any problems?

YES/NO

If you answered YES you should stop this test now, until you have a clean bill of health no licence will be issued to you.

If you answered NO you can go on to question C:

C) Do you now or have you ever suffered from mental illness?

YES/NO

If you've answered YES, this drug is not for you. No licence will be issued. If you've answered NO you may begin with question number one.

This Book

First

Cover the page with a piece of paper and pull it down line by line as you read, or have someone read the questions to you. Do this for the whole test. On your honour, no cheating, now begin.

PART TWO

1) When is the <u>only</u> time I should take a psychedelic trip ?

a) when I'm depressed

b) when I'm upset

c) when I'm already happy

d) any time is fine

Those who answered (a) or (b) or (d) read section on Psychedelics starting on page 117 to page 127 and start again. Those who answered (c) may continue to question two.

2) Should I have the urge that I can fly like Superman, where is the best place to try my ability?

a) from a small building

b) from a cliff

c) using only a small step ladder

d) from the ground up

Those who answered (a) or (b) or (c) turn to page 138 and examine the picture carefully, then start again with question two. Those who answered (d) can go on to question three.

3) Where is the best place for me to try tripping for the first time ?

a) at a rave

b) in a busy street

c) in a space I've lovingly prepared, with a good friend to keep an eye on me

d) while using dangerous machinery

Those who answered (a) or (b) or (d) read section on Psychedelics starting page 117 carefully, then turn to page 144 and read what you find **in bold,** then start again with question three. Those who answered (c) go on to question four.

4) For my first trip I should take:

a) one half a hit

b) all the trips I can afford

c) at least two to feel it

d) as much as will fit in a syringe

If you've answered (b) or (c) or (d) turn to page 144 and read the words *__in italics,__* then start again with question four. If you've answered (a) go on to question five.

5) While on my trip, if colours start to fill the air and the room starts to breathe I should:

a) panic

b) realise I'm tripping and enjoy it

c) call the police

d) open all the windows and doors to let the colours out

If you've answered (a) or (c) or (d) go quickly to page 142 and read the section *__in italics,__* then start again with question five. If you've answered (b) go on to question six.

6) If, while I'm tripping I see something that disturbs me I should:

a) throw things at it to make it go away

b) take deep breaths

c) ask my friend who has agreed to baby sit me if it's real or not

d) run as fast as I can towards it showing no fear

Those who answered (a) or (b) or (d) turn to page 121 and read the section *in italics,* then start again with question six. Those who answered (c) go on to question seven.

7) If I feel I'm not enjoying my trip and I'd like to stop, I should:

a) call 999

b) stand on my head and chant

c) run into the street yelling **stop** as loud as I can

d) take a couple of sleeping pills and go to the place I pre-pared to sleep

This Book

If you've answered (a) or (b) or (c) turn to page 124 and read carefully the section entitled. *The Easy Way Out*, then start again with question seven. If you've answered (d) go on to question eight.

8 The day after my trip I should:

a) take the day off

b) schedule a busy day

c) keep my eyes closed and avoid the sun

d) take some aspirin

If you've answered (b) or (c) or (d) go to page 123 and read the section ***in italics***, then start again with question eight. If you've answered (a) go on to question nine.

9) After my first trip I should:

a) take LSD every single day after

b) never look at a Magic Eye picture again

c) start taking Heroin

d) trip no more than once with each season

LSD

If you've answered (a) or (b) go to page 122 and read the section ***in italics*** then start again with question nine. If you've answered (c) read the section on Heroin starting page 81 as well as the above.

If you've answered (d) CONGRATULATIONS ! You have successfully passed this test.

You will be issued with a Provisional Futuristic Pretend Tripping Licence valid for the next seasons trip *with a baby sitter.*

You will find your *Licence to Trip* on the opposite page. Those who have genuinely passed this test *without cheating* may fill it out, *for the fun of it*, if you wish.

* * * * *

AN ADDED PRECAUTION
We are getting reports of liquid LSD as strong as that common in the 60's being offered on the streets, so take care.

LICENCE TO TRIP

A FUTURISTIC PRETEND RAINBOW LAND LICENCE

THIS IS TO CERTIFY THAT

NAME...

Has successfully passed the
THIS BOOK licence to trip test
and is therefore well informed
in the basic knowledge
needed for safe tripping
(while accompanied by a baby sitter)

*See other side
for details*

THE MINI * STAR OF PSYCHEDELICS

has produced the **Acid Test** in "This Book, The Truth About Drugs", and issues this licence to those who successfully pass *without cheating,* in the futuristic spirit of providing *real and fun education* as opposed to vindictive legislation to help avoid the possible dangers involved with the use of psychedelic drugs.

While this is a *pretend **Rainbow Land Licence*** created for *educational purposes only*, it is valid for the use of **legal psychedelics** today, such as Magic Mushrooms, Toad and raw DMT, but also covers important points concerning LSD, Psilocybin, STP and Mescaline, *should these become legal in the future.*

The use of DMT, while being legal, is not recommended without previous experience of less powerful mind expanding drugs.

In the futuristic spirit of *honour and trust*, the *Mini*Star of Psychedelics* asks each holder to pass the test before signing the following declaration to make their licence valid.

On my honour I declare that I have, without cheating, successfully passed the Licence To Trip Test set in "This Book, The Truth About Drugs", and have earned the right to be a "Licence To Trip" holder.

SIGNED..DATE...........................

Further copies of the Acid Test and This Licence can be obtained by ordering **"This Book, The Truth About Drugs"**
from **Those Publishers** P.O Box 10059
London NW2 6WR
including £9.99 cheque or postal order.

A licence is only as good as the common sense used by it's holder!

This Book

You'd have no problems to speak of with LSD or other psychedelics if you had to pass such a test before using them. Like with cars there might be some accidents but that's all they would be. Most of the hazards involved could be eliminated with this knowledge.

There are loads of clever people who have taken this stuff, and it's done them no harm at all. With careful use and in moderation this drug can cause you to be a better person because of the awareness it can awaken in you.

If you try to develop ideas you have on LSD, you'll be amazed at how many of them work. The idea of *Karma,* that you reap what you sow, and that the universe is some-how balanced, seems to be an easy one to grasp on LSD, and it works well in real life when you try it. What goes around inevitably does come around.

The philosophies of *Buddha* and of *Jesus* which include *Karma,* are easy to trip with. It's a very peaceful and joyful thing, from which sprung the modern peace movement. *Give Peace a Chance and All You Need is Love* are John Lennon *Acid* songs. These are the sort of things which people think about on Acid. The oneness of it all, the futility of war, the brotherhood of man, but more important, the stupidity of the people now running our world, which is the main reason this drug is outlawed by them.

This drug can only harm those who fail to pay it the respect that such a powerful substance deserves.

157

*Indian Brave" Little High Cloud" finally succeeds in flying
<u>from</u> <u>the</u> <u>ground</u> <u>up</u>, but he is slightly disappointed with his
animal spirit guide.*

MESCALINE

What Is It?
A hallucinogenic alkaloid
found in mescal buttons
which grow on the peyote
cactus, which can be eaten
or chewed, also produced
in tablet and capsule form.

Other Names:
Peyote

Where Does It Come From?
Peyote cactus plants grow mainly in desert regions of the
U.S.A. and Mexico.

What Does It Cost?
Free for the picking or £5 to £15 per capsule or tablet.

What Does It Do?
Mescaline creates a gentle yet very powerful psychedelic
experience lasting up to 12 hours.
Users experience an extreme sense of calm, as if a calm
bubble has landed to surround them. It is near impossible
to find a sharp edge while on this drug as even things
which normally look pointed reveal their round atomic
edges

Mescaline

It can make it's users feel in tune with time. Where as normally you might feel rushed with only ten minutes to a deadline, on this drug it seems like there is loads of time as you prepare, even if you complete your preparations with only a second to spare.

Peyote has played an important part in the North American Indian's culture for centuries. It is part of the right of passage ceremony which a young male would experience in becoming a man.

Before this all important trip, the young brave, in his preparation would be told by an experienced Shaman to look out for certain things which would influence the rest of his life. He would look for an animal which would become his spirit guide, he might speak to his ancestors to get guidance and he might even see the future and the part he must play within it.

Taken in a natural setting this experience would serve as a bonding process with nature. This drug is well known for it's ability to bring out the beauty in nature and amplifies the user's oneness with all of life.

Precautions
All the advice in the Psychedelic Drugs section and the Licence To Trip Test applies here.

Much of what is presented as Mescaline isn't.

This Book

Here are some tips on how to recognise the real thing if it's not being offered to you by an Indian fresh from the plant, (which would be ideal).

In garden shops you can buy plant pots made of compressed peat which are a small disc which grows into a small pot when you put water on them, (Grow Pots). Real mescaline mostly comes in a large tablet as round as a penny which look in substance very much like this compressed peat. When in capsules these are generally quite large and you can still see brown fibres.

While for the most part this drug is mellow, it is also very strong, so be prepared for a complete experience.

This is not too common in the U.K. but should you find yourself where it is in plentiful supply, it would still be best kept for special occasions, as has been done by those who have used this drug as a spiritual aide for centuries.

Government's Opinion
Illegal Class A (see section on Drug Classes page 31)

Author's Opinion
When Columbus arrived in America he found the Indians taking care of the entire continent like it was one big park or heath. They lived as part of nature. These people understood the *Holy Spirit of Life* in an intimate way.

Mescaline

They took only what they needed and used all which they took. These people had the techniques of ecological living down pat.

If the white mad men had been loving towards these people, they could have shared their knowledge and we probably would not be hearing about our world in eco crisis today.

How much was the taking of Mescaline responsible for the Indian's respect for Life? That we cannot really answer, but we can say without a doubt that it played an important part.

TO THINK OR NOT TO THINK?

Sit with a group of people smoking Cannabis, and as the joints and pipes get passed around, sooner or later someone will mention the law. And someone else might point out how silly and hypocritical the banning of Cannabis is. "OK for them to go down the pub, but not OK for us to have a smoke."

By the time someone throws in how Cannabis is known to be less harmful than alcohol, we have a full blown discussion on how the people running the country are not fit to do the job.

Recent stories on corruption take the floor. The difference between murder and war might come in, and unchecked pollution and government kick backs might get a mention. This group is now asking questions few would have dared to ask 50 years ago.

People on Tranquillisers tend to be loners in their drug taking. They don't as a rule get together to pop their pills.

To Think or Not To Think

They don't question the way things are, they take these pills to cope with what is unchangeable to them. They don't go on protest marches.

The housewife and businessman on Valium do their best to complete the task at hand. They have been prescribed these pills to mask the stress of it all. They use these drugs as a hiding place for their problems, not a soap box to express their views.

The raver taking a psychedelic drug finds he is surrounded by friendly loving people all having fun. Later he or she will talk about the good vibes and friendly atmosphere. "If anyone so much as bumped into you, they said sorry and offered you something. It was like we all knew each other really well" they'll say. And inevitably someone will say, "shame it can't be like that all the time", and someone else might point out that armies and police forces are not all that friendly.

They speak from personal experience. They will use as an example the police who came in with riot gear to stop the them from dancing. The contrast of attitudes will make the memory of this special time complete.

These ravers will also be asking questions few would have dared to ask 50 years ago. "Who are these *kill-joys* running the country and how can they ban what they know nothing about?" might be one of them.

DMT

What Is It?
A chemical who's full name is Dimethyltryptamine, found naturally in some plants (and toads), or processed as white powdery crystals, (eaten or smoked in a pipe, on a bed of dried mint).

Other Names:
Businessman's acid, Businessman's lunch, Yopo

Where Does It Come From?
Africa, South America and the West Indies, discovered by native indians. It is noted in the journals of Christopher Columbus' second voyage to America in 1496.

DMT is also naturally found in the human lung, brain, cerebrospinal fluid, liver and heart.

What Does It Cost?
£300 per gram £20 to £40 per dose (1/16 to 1/8 of a gram)

DMT

What Does It Do?

This drug produces a full blown psychedelic trip within moments after smoking it which lasts up to 15 minutes. It needs to be taken sitting down!

Users report the sensation of swimming in a *psychedelic soup* almost instantly upon smoking it.

The effects are much stronger and more intense than that of LSD or Mushrooms. Some previous knowledge of strong psychedelics is desirable, as a novice might be overwhelmed.

Trips vary from outside to indoors. Outside among nature it inspires a fairy tale experience. Users report being in the company of fairies and goblins. Time seems to speed up and the 15 minutes seem shorter than usual.

Indoors - Things rush by. Users have reported seeing silver faces which brush against them as they pass. Colours become very bright especially purples and yellows with a lot of silver appearing, like that seen on the scales of fish. It's like seeing a *psychedelic tartan* which is continuously changing.

The dimensions of the room can alter radically, with the floor seeming very close and the ceiling seeming miles away, for instance.

Hallucinations can be shared by a group. You seem to be able to see into different dimensions. Some users are convinced this is actually happening.

You are likely to lose control of your motor senses, making natural movements a chore. This is definitely one to sit back and enjoy.

It has been used by South American Indians for centuries, inhaled like snuff to produce a spiritual experience.

Users comment: "It is overwhelming, and if you enjoy psychedelics, it is overwhelmingly good. It feels like someone has unzipped your face and your whole life's memory flops out of your head."

After about 15 minutes the experience begins to fade and after 45 minutes or so you are completely back to normal with no ill effects and no trace in your system.

This is not an addictive drug, but the experience can be repeated the same day, being just as strong, unlike with LSD.

PRECAUTIONS
Do not try this unless you have previous experience with other psychedelics.

DMT

Although this is a short trip, it is really intense. Do not do it on your own. If possible be accompanied by an experienced user you can trust.

Use in controlled surroundings; not recommended for use at a rave, for example. Sit somewhere comfortably and expect to stay there for the extent of the trip.

If you have any history of mental disorder this drug is not for you.

It's powder form makes it difficult to know what you are getting, see Powders page 59).

It really needs to be acquired from someone familiar with it that you can trust. It is currently rare in the U.K. but because it is not illegal in it's raw plant or animal form, that might well change soon, (or they might make it totally illegal, which will boost it's popularity no end).

Those with previous experience with other psychedelics should refresh their memory by doing the *Licence to Trip Test* starting on page 147, leaving out question 7. Be sure you understand each question and can pass easily without cheating.

(see Serious Health Warnings page 35)

This Book

Government's Opinion
It is legal in it's raw form. Plants containing DMT can be purchased mail order from Of the Jungle, PO Box 1801 Sebastopol CA 95473 USA, and found in toads. (page 171)

The processed chemical is class A, but even the Home Office is vaguely aware of this and sometimes claims it's unlisted. As for the plants, there are only 3 plants mentioned in the misuse of drugs act. They are cannabis, coca, and the opium poppy, non of which contain DMT.

Author's Opinion
If it has any enlightening qualities and it's fun the *kill-joys* are bound to want to ban these plants as well.

All the suggestions for the preparation of a trip apply here except for the sleeping pills *easy way out*. By the time the pills start to work, your trip will be over anyway.

No one steps into a formula one racing car and puts their foot down to tear round the track before learning how to drive an ordinary car first. It would be just as silly to use this drug as a first time introduction to psychedelics. Mushrooms are the thing for that.

In the words of a user and fan, "when you think you have experienced it all is the time to try it. Fasten your seat belts for Warp Factor 8". This drug's use by South American Indians to produce a spiritual experience tells me it should be treated with respect and only used on special occasions.

TOAD

What Is It?
It is Colorado River Toad venom (bufo alvarius) dried. Also the dried skin of some toads, and can also be acquired by licking the sap from a cane toads back.

Other Names:
Magic Toad, 5-MeO-DMT, witches' brew ingredient, and PsychoKermit.

Where Does It Come From?
Colorado River, Arizona Desert, some deserts in Australia.

The venom of the Colorado River Toad is very dangerous when fresh, and can kill within minutes by paralysing the respiratory system. When dried it becomes a hallucinogenic substance. Other Toads are skinned and dried into a powder which is smoked, while the lucky ones can be licked and set loose producing the same effect.

Toad

Fresh Venom is easy to collect without hurting the toad. Use a plate of glass about 12 inches square. Place it vertically in front of the toad. Holding the toad firmly with one hand, use your thumb and forefinger to squeeze near the base of the glands found on the legs, and neck. Each gland can be squeezed a second time after an hour. Once empty they take about six weeks to replenish.

The milky-white venom is then scraped off the glass and dried thoroughly.

What Does It Cost?
Free if you can catch one, (apart from the plane fare to Arizona or Australia).

What Does It Do?
This produces a full blown psychedelic trip lasting 3 to 4 hours, (see section on Psychedelics page 117). It has been described as an "*astral propellant*" for it's apparent ability to lift one to different dimensions.

Some claim the Frog which turned into a Prince after being kissed by the Princess in the fairy tale was a story inspired by a hallucination actually experienced after a girl kissed a Magic Toad?

Toad venom contains 5-Me0-DMT. DMT has it's own chapter in "This Book", (see page 165 for details if you haven't already).

This Book

DMT multiplies the brains activity many times over and is a very psychoactive substance .

PRECAUTIONS
Not recommended if you have no previous experience of other psychedelics. Also if you have any history of mental illness this drug is not for you.

Do not use it on your own. If possible be with an experienced user you can trust. Be ready to just sit back in the desert and watch what happens.

It's powder form makes it difficult to know for sure that it's Toad you are getting, unless you catch your own, or can really trust your supplier, (see Powders page 59 if you haven't already).

Venom must be COMPLETELY DRY or it can be deadly.

Vegetarians should seek out the licking variety which does not involve the killing of an innocent amphibian.

Should you make the trip to Arizona or Australia, it would be wise to seek out advice from those in the know, who will probably be happy to share their knowledge and experience, as psychedelic fans often are.

Research on Toads will disclose their hallucinogenic aspects and also provide colour pictures for easier identification, (see your library).

Toad

Use only small amounts as this is very powerful.

Be sure to review the *Licence to Trip Test* starting on page 147 and be sure you can pass easily before starting out. (see Serious Health Warnings page 35)

Government's Opinion

There are no laws concerning Magic Toads in the U.K. apart from the usual laws against cruelty to animals. We could not find 5-Me0-DMT mentioned in any legislation. The drying of toad venom might be considered processing of the DMT part found in it, but being rare in the UK, we have no test cases to refer to. This is as yet a gray area.

Author's Opinion

If you did go to the expense and trouble of travelling out to Arizona to find a Colorado River Toad, then it would be worth doing it right. Seek out a guide who can steer you right and insure you get the real thing to stay out of danger. "Seek and you will find."

While this one really is reserved for connoisseurs of psychedelics, preparation should not be ignored.

It's funny to think about a psychedelic hit hopping it's way around the desert, but then "God does work in mysterious ways". This produces a powerful experience suitable only for special occasions, not constant use. **Treat with respect.**

174

STP

What Is It?
It is an amphetamine based hallucinogenic that works on the nervous system.

Other Names:
Dimethoxymethamphetamine, DOM

Where Does It Come From?
It was discovered in America, synthesised in laboratories as a biological weapon by the U.S. military intended for use in the Vietnam War.

Once known the chemical formula got around to be produced for recreational use.

What Does It Cost?
£5 to £10 a hit.

STP

What Does It Do?

It produces a hallucinogenic trip lasting from 12 to 72 hours depending on the strength. It is similar to Acid but the effects are a lot stronger and it lasts a lot longer, being more visually stimulating.

It comes on in peaks and troughs (in waves). You might climb to a peak, come down and think it is over then find yourself climbing once again like being on a roller coaster ride of rushes.

Things seem to transform for the user. People can change into different characters. It seems to stretch and re-shape reality making people look like clay models you can mould.

The actual peaks create a very thick display of colours which might be hard to see through. It's very powerful and it's effects are as a drug and not as a catalyst, meaning you can take larger doses getting even longer trips, as this is relying on *itself* to produce it's effects and not the natural chemicals in the brain as in the case of LSD.

You would not be likely to want to repeat the experience too often, it being so overwhelming. The body does create a tolerance if this drug is taken several days in a row, which means more and more needs to be taken to produce the same effects.

This fact in itself is enough to discourage constant use.

It can be an enlightening experience, but merits good preparation to be positive, it's effects being similar to a mix between LSD and Ecstacy providing both good feelings and colourful hallucinations, but for a much longer period.

PRECAUTIONS
Do the *Licence to Trip Test* (page 147) and be sure you pass without cheating.

Be prepared for a really intense experience.

Not a drug for anyone with mental health problems.

Some previous experience with less strong psychedelics is recommended.

(see Serious Health Warnings page 35)

Government's Opinion
Illegal Class A, (see section on Drug Classes page 31)

Author's Opinion
You really do need to take some time off for this one.

Rave On !

ECSTASY AND EAVES

What Is It?

A synthetic chemical called MDMA which is short for Methylene Dioxy Meth Amphetamine, which can be eaten, smoked and is sometimes injected, or MDEA, which is Methylene Dioxy Ethyl Amphetamine, a slight variation created to beat the law which soon caught up to include it on the Class A list.

Other Names:

MDMA, E's, XTC. EAVES MDEA Various brand names include, Doves, Love Doves, Burgers, Rhubarb and Custard New yorkers, Denis the Menace, M25's Dutch Splitbacks, Pink White and Yellow Cali, Jurassic Parks, Double Bubbles, Banana splits, Cali Dreamers, Pink Cadillac, Fido Dido and many more.

Ecstacy and Eves

Where Does It Come From?
It was first produced in 1910 in Europe as MDA, (the parent drug).

This drug was considered by the U.S. military to be used in chemical warfare. The loving feelings this substance inspires probably explains why they abandoned this approach.

Up until the mid 80's you could buy Ecstacy over the counter in bars and clubs all over the U.S.A.. Each dose was sold with a set of flight instructions written in a little booklet which explained how to enjoy the drug without getting into problems with it.

Also in America, marriage therapists began using MDMA to bring rowing couples together again, with great success. Rumour has it that some couples even faked their rows to get the treatment again, long after it had been successful. Someone in the *kill-joy* department must have noticed them smiling, because it was duly banned in 1985 in the U.S.A..

Today it is produced by illegal labs mainly in Holland, California, and Britain.

Much of what is presented as Ecstacy isn't MDMA at all. Instead a user might get crude Heroin, dirty Speed, Ketamine, Ephedrine (a cough mixture), Selegiline (prescribed to old people for Parkinson's disease) or even

Caffeine. And some might contain rough forms of MDA from which MDMA comes, which could be cut with any number of things. Other things which have been sold as "E" include aspirin, fish tank tablets, hay fever pills, or just chalk.

What Does It Cost?
£10 to £20 per capsule or tablet

What Does It Do?
It creates a feeling of Love and intimacy for anyone who might to be with you. Part of ancient Hindu belief is that there are centres within the body which control various emotions and urges which they call *Chakras*. Pure MDMA seems to open up the centres responsible for the Love we feel for other people. Western world romantics would say it opens up your heart.

Pure MDMA can affect the user in two main and different ways. A user might be inspired to dance the night away, while a romantic couple might be content to cuddle in a quiet corner, hardly moving at all. Each will experience a warmth which seems to be generated by the presence of others.

The user's sense of touch is made more sensitive, which can enhance love making. It increases your heart rate. Vision can seem to vibrate as the drug starts to take effect. Also people on E can acquire a very convincing gift of the gab.

Ecstacy and Eves

This is a mild hallucinogenic drug, which means you might see a pale tint of colour in the air, but not much more than that. It is borderline between a psychedelic and a stimulant.

None of the problems associated with bad trips apply here. Pure MDMA lifts you gently into a warm sphere for about 4 hours and then gently drops you back again. Some people report feeling depressed the next day. Others feel tired but fine.

The tabloid press has boasted headlines of people dying from taking Ecstacy. While we could note that, out of the thousands of airplanes which land safely, only the one which crashes makes the headlines, there is actually more to these stories than just sensationalism, if we read carefully between the lines.

Where it is known that some people have died after taking *what they thought* was pure MDMA there has never been any proof that it was pure MDMA which they took.

As mentioned before, the parent drug, MDA has been around since 1910. It had a large cult following, being openly sold in the 60's with no reports of death from it's normal use, and we know therapists used MDMA to treat distressed married couples again with no deaths reported. It is worth noting here that the MDMA used by therapists was produced by pharmaceutical companies to an exact standard.

182

It is possible to overdose on MDMA but this is not the cause given for recent deaths. We are told deaths reported were a result of dehydration or something causing blood to build up in the lungs. Drug Help agencies advocate drinking a pint of water or soft drinks every hour to prevent heat stroke. This advice is worth taking when we consider that our married couples being treated probably didn't dance through each session. As for the blood coagulation problems, this is a relatively new phenomenon, which is more likely caused by something which has been mixed with MDMA to increase it's weight and value.

If there was something in pure MDMA which causes fatal internal problems, this would likely have been discovered years ago, and in general most if not all the people taking the drugs would be affected. Needless to say, it would not be very popular. But when we consider it is estimated that over a million doses are taken every week causing no such problems, it makes it more and more likely that something added by an unscrupulous dealer is responsible for these isolated incidents.

It is also possible that some people are allergic to MDMA as some people can be to Cocaine.

PRECAUTIONS
Recent deaths involving people who thought they were taking Ecstacy are real cause for concern here.

Ecstacy and Eves

Whether it was pure MDMA they took, or some back street chemist's concoction being sold as Ecstacy is open to debate. What we are sure of is that these deaths were isolated incidents, and the great majority of people who have tried Ecstacy have had no problems with it.

We are told the deaths which were a result of *heat stroke* happened because of dehydration, and could have been avoided if the users had drunk at least one pint of water or soft drinks each hour, (what one tends to lose while dancing).

If you go out dancing on "E", bring bottles of fresh water with you. If that is not allowed, be sure to drink plenty of liquids anyway.

The drug and the music might make you forgetful and make time fly, so why not make a game out of reminding people in your group to have a drink.

If you are not with a group, just remind the person next to you and ask them to remind you. You'll have no problem talking to them in sign language if the music is too loud.

Also have a rest from dancing regularly.

HEAT STROKE

Be on the lookout for heat stroke warning signs, such as:
(1) Failure to sweat.

(2) Heat cramps in your arms, legs and back.

(3) Dizziness, feeling tired or experiencing headaches.

(4) Vomiting.

(5) Problems urinating, producing small amounts, highly coloured.

(6) Passing out.

If someone does pass out, **seek medical help to administer CPR if they are not breathing.**

If they are breathing well, make an effort to cool them down by getting them outside perhaps, drenching them with water, fanning air on them or cooling them in any way you can think of.

If your efforts revive the person, have them drink water, with a pinch of salt, if you can find some. Try to arrange for some dry clothing (even a blanket if nothing else is available). If they remain unconscious have someone call an ambulance and stay with them until it arrives.

Ecstacy and Eves

As for the possibility that some people may be allergic to MDMA, with it being made illegal all the research which might have found a way to test this safely has gone out the window.

So small amounts to begin with has to be safer than large amounts. Wait for the effects before taking any more. People have been overwhelmed by taking more thinking the first bit wasn't working when it was just about to kick in.

Eating a meal after taking "E" helps balance your system and also provides necessary liquids.

Once a tablet is pressed, it is not likely to be tampered with. You then rely on the integrity of the producer for quality. In powder form such as that in gelatin capsules, chances are this drug has been *cut* several times before being offered to the end user. Re- read the section on Powders page 59; you may find that the This Book Powders Poison Test is very appropriate here. As mentioned there, in Amsterdam there facilities available to test for the actual contents of a powder.

This is my first and only comment directly *TO DEALERS,* which I'd like you to listen in on. "If you intend to purchase a quantity of pills or powder claiming to be MDMA, it would be worth your consciences' peace to **have a sample tested in Amsterdam .**"

186

This Book

This might prove too expensive for the individual, but use your imagination. *You could have a pool among friends where each chips in a portion for a mini lottery and the winner gets to go to Amsterdam to do the test.*

Warning: (while you only need a small scraping to accomplish this safety measure, you could still be done for possession if that chip is discovered by the authorities).

Also, **very good news!** In the UK, the Green Party Drugs Group and Dylan Trump of EZ Test do market kits which detect the presence of MDMA (ecstasy) which cost about £10. The 'drugs tzar' Keith Hellawell, appointed by the government to oversee drugs policy, on BBC Radio 4's Today programme (May 27 1998), described these as 'immoral'. *(which makes them worth looking into).*

Also, here are a few home tests you can do to establish if it's E you have or something else. While these are not as reliable as a lab test or the kits,, they are worth knowing so I list them here.

Burn a bit. Real MDMA has a liquorish smell when burnt. Burning a bit on foil will melt it into a white bubbly substance and usually leaves a red residue. If burning produces a bad smell, not unlike burnt socks, you've probably got speed.

Ecstacy and Eves

It's also worth noting that real "E" makes the pupils of your eyes dilate, but if it's mixed with Heroin, your pupils get smaller. So if you see a bunch of ravers with pinned eyes, ask what they've taken and avoid it. Heroin makes you rush and people who don't know better can mistake this for an "E" rush.

Also if "E" dancing ravers are reporting severe hallucinations they are probably on LSD.

Mixing "E" with other drugs like Temazapam or Valium can be dangerous. Don't mix "E" with other drugs as a rule.

People with heart problems should avoid this drug, as should people with high blood pressure, anyone subject to epileptic fits or any kind of mental illness.

Long term use can cause damage to your kidneys and liver.

If injecting, do not share needles to avoid spreading diseases.

Too much "E" can reduce the levels of serotonin in your brain, which can cause mood swings. If this starts to happen you definitely should **give it a break** to let your brain chemistry get back into balance.

Taking vitamins after dancing all night is a good idea to replace what you use up.

This drug has a toxic level which makes it possible to over-dose, so don't eat handfuls of the stuff, even if they're offered. (see section on Serious Health Warnings page 35)

Government's Opinion
Both MDMA and MDEA are illegal Class A, (see section on Drug Classes page 31).

Author's Opinion
The making of something illegal automatically closes the door to the development of health and safety standards where this is concerned. The extensive tests and studies which could be done to make something more and more safe to take grind to a halt.

While things sold legally need to meet high health and safety standards, things sold on the black market do not. For the most part, things sold legally in shops can be relied upon to contain what is stated on the label. This includes pharmaceutical drugs which can be obtained on prescription.

The real concern we have here is that a drug which makes most people who take it feel good about themselves and others is also being blamed for the death of an isolated few; and because of the legal situation no research is being done to establish the *real cause* of these deaths. In the vacuum of no studies, we are left guessing, which is not really very satisfactory at all.

Ecstacy and Eves

It is typical of our current leaders to just turn the lights out and shut the door, as if that is the solution to the problem.

Like putting a plaster on a dirty cut without washing and disinfecting it first. From the outside the problem seems solved as all you can see is the shinny new plaster, but underneath the infection continues to fester, helped by the heat the plaster creates.

While information and scientific observation can help solve a problem, legislation just drives the problem underground, removing the incentive for finding a real solution.

The lawmakers, far from being in control, *actually lose control* when they ban something.

When it was legal, doctors prescribing MDMA were confident in it's purity, and there were no deaths from heat dehydration or blood coagulation. Now it is illegal a back street chemist can experiment with mixtures and perhaps change their recipe if they hear of people dying, while governments can blame the deaths on Ecstacy, to justify their laws, when it was probably something else that caused the problem.

In it's pure form, if that can be established, this drug should be treated in the same way as a psychedelic and used only on special occasions.

MDA

What Is It?
Methylene Dioxy Amphetamine, the head of a family of drugs known as Phenthlamines or PEA's for short.

Other Names:
Snowballs, Mellow Drug of America.

Where Does It Come From?
First made in Europe in 1910. Now produced in illegal labs mainly in Britain, Holland, and California.

What Does It Cost?
Often sold as MDMA, (Ecstacy), at the same price of between £10 and £20 per capsule or tablet.

MDA

What Does It Do?
A high dose of MDA is more like an LSD type experience, and not what you might expect from "E". There is a trippy-ness about it which does not occur with it's offspring MDMA or MDEA.

It has a high toxic level making the dangers of overdose very real. As few as 3 Snowballs can take you into the danger zone.

Users are more prone to want to sit the next few dances out, experiencing heavy rushes. Ravers finding themselves on MDA when they expected Ecstacy might make good use of a chill out room, taking deep breaths and having a drink, (not alcohol).

It can cause excessive dilation of the pupil in the eye.

A mild overdose causes arms and legs to become rigid and breathing becomes uneasy.

Recent tests have shown that the average snow ball contains about 180 mg of MDA which is a fairly high dosage that will set off an intense experience. Not being ready for it can be the main problem and adapting to it quickly the best solution, (see next section).

PRECAUTIONS

Most people who take MDA these days do so unknowingly expecting it to be MDMA.

If your "E" starts to come on like a trip, you start to feel weak and need to take deep breaths, get off the dance floor and into a more relaxed environment where it's cooler, drink some water or non-alcoholic drink and try to relax and enjoy it.

Do not try to make an "E" experience out of it, realise it's something different, a much more laid back buzz.

Review the Heat Stroke warnings in the Ecstacy section (page 185) and be on the lookout for the signs. At first warning, cool off.

Staying calm is vital as over excitement can cause the user to go into convulsions.

Taking MDA by choice when MDMA or MDEA are available is comparable to having fish fingers when you can have salmon, (*not very clever*).

Government's Opinion
This is a Class A drug.

(see section on Drug Classes, page 31)

MDA

Author's Opinion

Clever chemists took a look at MDA and discovered that by making a few changes the rough edges could be removed from the effects of the drug. What they produced is a drug which is more gentle and enjoyable than the original. It's new design bought us the phrase *"Designer Drugs"*.

These chemists were heading in the right direction but any further progress they might have made has been (temporarily?) halted by the law.

Surely, instead of trying to ban drugs, which never eliminates them anyway, the way forward should be to produce safer and safer drugs, allowing the user enjoyment without unwanted side effects. With the improvements which have been made hardly anyone would want to have the old unimproved product anymore.

But being in the illegal, no quality control domain, MDA still shows up pretending to be superior MDMA or MDEA and people end up with an experience they didn't expect, which is a shame but not the end of the world so long as it's not too strong and they don't take too many.

Be aware that MDA is still around, take care and be ready to change your game plan accordingly if you find yourself on some.

JUSTICE OR JUST THEM?

DRUGS,
THE COURTS AND CIRCUMSTANTIAL EVIDENCE

Anyone who has been convicted of a crime is no longer eligible to sit on a jury.

Have you ever wondered why?

Anyone who has been on the receiving end of the judicial system will tell you that there are many things which go on in the process which the general public know nothing about. Most people, for instance, still believe that *actual evidence* is needed to secure a conviction. But a browse through court records would confirm that many people today are convicted on circumstantial evidence alone.

There was a time when cases resting on circumstantial evidence would not make it to trial, being thrown out at the committal stage, but now more and more, juries are being left to decide what is relevant and what is not, when no real proof exists. This turns the whole process into a guessing game.

Justice or Just Them?

HOW IT WORKS

Circumstantial evidence can easily lead one to the wrong conclusion, and with the accused in the dock to begin with, it's easy for the average person to assume that they must be guilty. "If they are not guilty, why have they been arrested?". Recent well publicised miscarriages of justice seem to have done little to change this well ingrained attitude.

To explain how unreliable circumstantial evidence can be, let me use a simple example. Say you and I are in a room and you are reading "*This Book*". I see what you are reading and comment that I'd like to read it sometime myself. You are called out, so you put the book down and go for twenty minutes. When you return I'm gone and the book is gone.

From the evidence you have you might easily conclude that it was *me* who took the book. After all, I did say I'd like to read it, I was left there alone with it, and both it and I are now gone.

But there are any number of thing which might have happened during the time that you were gone. One possibility is that I left right after you and someone else spotted the book and took it before you returned. But in a court of law, that would be an unfounded suggestion, whereas the conclusion that it was me who took the book would be based on the facts you saw.

This Book

In a case like this, a Judge would tell the Jury that they could use inference to decide my innocence or guilt. Inference is just a fancy word for guessing when you don't know all the facts.

NOT MY PROBLEM
You might well feel that all of this has little to do with you or our chosen subject drugs, but consider this.

In this country alone there are millions of people involved with illegal drugs in one way or another, and you don't need to actually handle drugs to be convicted of conspiracy to supply them.

If a drug dealer under surveillance by the police visits your home, the police don't need *proof* that you were involved in a drug deal to take you to Court, and you might well wait over a year on remand, in Prison, before your case even comes to trial; (people who are supposed to be "innocent until proven guilty" get locked up every day).

You might feel that the solution is simply not to offer any hospitality to drug dealers, but drug dealers tend to work on a need to know basis, so unless you really are involved, you might never know about your guest's illegal habits. Why should they risk telling you if it's really no concern of yours?

Justice or Just Them?

Perhaps you think if a dealer was arrested in your home, and you were not involved, they would instantly tell the police of your innocence. Don't count on it!

CAN YOU TELL THE DIFFERENCE?

But surely, after a year or so awaiting trail in prison, no jury could ever find you guilty. There is after all no real evidence against you. Surely *anyone* can see the difference between real evidence and circumstantial evidence.

You think so? Well let's try a little test to prove that theory.

LSD commonly comes on paper printed with designs. Pretend you, on a jury, are presented with a sheet of LSD paper which has on it the unmistakable fingerprint of the accused. What can you safely conclude from this? The defendant has handled and was therefore involved with this LSD?

Not necessarily so. LSD is usually applied to paper in a solution of alcohol, and what do they use in the process of bringing up finger prints on paper? Alcohol!

In actual fact a finger print can easily survive the making of LSD process and could have been placed there long before that paper ever became LSD.

The friend you never suspected of being a drug dealer might have left some innocent art paper on your table and you moved it to prepare for a meal. Days or weeks later and maybe miles away from your home, while this same paper is being converted into LSD, your finger print is still with it clear as day.

THE BARRISTER'S TALE
Add that finger print to the fact that you received a visit from a known dealer added to the impression of you standing in the dock after months of imprisonment, and a well trained barrister can spin a yarn good enough to get your own mother to convict you. Like a musician or D.J. knows exactly what tunes to play to get their audience going, so these barristers know exactly what words to use to lead the jury towards a conviction. Its their job and many are expert at it.

If the courts had to rely on real evidence as opposed to circumstantial evidence they would need more than a dealer's visit to your home or a finger print on LSD paper to convict you. They would need someone to testify that they actually saw you handling or dealing drugs or a video showing you being involved. In other words "real proof".

HOW LONG HAS THIS BEEN GOING ON?
There has definitely been a change in how the legal system works. It is a change which has happened without fanfare. No-one had a chance to vote about it, and no bill was ever passed to support it or protest against it.

Yet this fundamental change has completely undermined any idea of *real* justice. So cleverly was this one slipped in, that it is near impossible to point to the time and place when this unjust practice started. We can't say when it started, but we can say, on the day it did everyone's real hope of a just legal system ended and we all became potential victims.

This change, to allow people with only circumstantial evidence against them to stand trial, has turned the Court system into a mockery of justice. While this system lasts, there are none of us who are safe from it, even in our own homes.

PRIVACY

If the police do suspect you of being involved with drugs, then they will *grant themselves permission* to search through all of your personal things. Every inch of what you thought was private will be examined by a bunch of strangers, some of them in uniform.

You might be taken to police cells which are designed to be oppressive.

No matter that they may have been watching people come and go from your home, if they find anything, even in your back garden, they will claim it is yours and you might have a six month wait in prison before you get to explain at your committal why you should not go to trial.

Justice or Just Them?

NO DRUGS FOUND!

What they find does not have to be drugs for them to charge you. It could be brand new envelopes or bags similar to some in which drugs have been found in the past. It could even be a phone number you innocently received.

At committal it can become clear that all the evidence against you is circumstantial, and if we were aspiring to any real form of justice, at this stage the case would be thrown out and you would be entitled to compensation.

But more and more, these cases go to trial and the jury is given permission to convict on assumption alone, by the judge who will sentence you if they do.

GUILT LATER ADMITTED

Some might point out that a large number of people convicted who pleaded not guilty later do admit their crime, so in many cases the system is right after all. But this ceases to be an impressive statistic when we are told that it is common practice for the parole officials to demand that a person admit their crime *before* agreeing to free them on parole; (for many this can make a difference of several years actual prison time).

So one of the systems strongest points of vindication is in fact extracted from people with force under duress and does not really qualify to be taken seriously at all.

This Book

WHO ARE THEY?
The idea of man made justice is an illusion, while the possibility of wrong convictions is very real.

The drug laws, which bring so many millions of people into an illegal circle are not just the concern of those interested in drugs. They are also the concern of all those that these millions come in contact with, and who *they* are is always a mystery because the nature of the occupation is to be in disguise, telling only those who really need to know.

Allowing conviction on circumstantial evidence alone has never been put to the vote. This is a liberty the courts have taken which they should be brought to task about.

This may well lead us to ask, were they ever really given the right to judge in the first place, or did they just take it against the good advice of Christ?

(THE AUTHOR SPEAKS FROM PERSONAL EXPERIENCE. ON FEBRUARY. 1ST 1991 HE WAS ARRESTED AND CHARGED WITH CONSPIRACY TO SUPPLY LSD. IN MAY 1992 HE WAS FOUND GUILTY *ON CIRCUMSTANTIAL EVIDENCE ALONE* AND RECEIVED A TEN YEAR PRISON SENTENCE.)

GHB

What Is It?
Gamma hydroxy butyrate or sodium oxybate, which is a colourless and odourless liquid with a slightly salty taste produced in bottles, to be taken internally; (also known to come in powder or capsules).

Other Names:
Liquid Ecstacy, GBH, Liquid X, Liquid E

Where Does It Come From?
From America and Europe. It was developed as a medical anaesthetic and more recently used as a growth hormone stimulant.

This operating theatre anaesthetic became popular with body builders in the late 80's who saw it as a means of muscle growth without Steroids. Psychedelic effects were reported and sales soared from health food shops until in 1991 it was banned in the U.S.A..

GHB

What Does It Cost?
£10 to £15 per bottle or £5 per cap full.

What Does It Do?
It works as a sedative taking effect after anything from 15 minutes to an hour of drinking it.

In small doses it can make the user feel happy and less inhibited. In larger doses it brings on sleep and has caused some people to go into a coma. People suffering from coma symptoms all seem to recover as the effects of the drug wear off and there had been no recorded deaths from taking GHB until one person died on February 10th 1999. This unfortunate death was reported to have been caused by mixing the drug with alcohol.

Used on the dance floor, combined with Amphetamines, it produces a high lasting 5 hours or so.

It is not clear what the correct dosage is, so how it will affect you is very much hit or miss. Slightly overdoing it can cause nausea, vomiting and muscle convulsions. Given the right balance, (which can only be guessed at), it produces effects which have been compared as a cross between Ecstasy and LSD. The tactile sensations are similar with GHB. Sound and vision distortions are commonly experienced.

PRECAUTIONS
Do not mix with alcohol.

The difference between a good time and ending up in a coma or dead depends on the amount taken; and the effects can vary from person to person. It would therefore follow that a sensible precaution to take, should you decide to try this drug, is to use only small amounts, increasing the dose only slightly after giving the drug **at least an hour** to take effect. Guzzling this drug until it comes on is not a good idea.

Having someone with you not partaking, baby sitting, is always a good idea.

As you might end up going to sleep, have a place to crash ready, even if it is just a blanket and pillow in the back seat of a car.

It would be best to establish an agreeable dose by trying small amounts in a controlled environment such as your home, before venturing out, to avoid collapsing in public.

Government's Opinion
Not a controlled substance but it is classed as a medicine, so unauthorised production is illegal under the Medicines Act.

It is not illegal to possess or take GHB in the U. K..

GHB

Authors Opinion

Laws against Ecstacy make it likely that what is produced as "E" will be contaminated with undesirable mixes. So what might be seen as a purer, legal substitute comes into demand. If all things were equal, GHB would not hold a candle to pure MDMA and hardly anyone would risk going into a coma or dying to produce a simular high to what Ecstacy produces without that risk.

As it is, the law makes the production of *pure* MDMA less and less likely, and people might well think, why risk prison taking a Class A drug which might not be pure when you can take GHB legally and only risk a temporary coma and a slim chance of death?

Unless you ban absolutely everything, there will always be substitutes produced to fill in for banned substances. They might not be as good or as safe, but they will continue to pop up like weeds to fill the gaps produced by legislation.

GHB is a medical anaesthetic which has been dusted out of the cupboard to fill in for MDMA. If MDMA had remained legal, I doubt anyone would be bothering with GHB. Handle with care if at all.

KETAMINE

What Is It?
Ketamine Hydrochloride in powder. capsule and tablet form, (eaten or snorted).

Other Names:
Special K, K,

Where Does It Come From?
Mostly from the U.S.A..

What Does It Cost?
£5 to £15 a hit.

What Does It Do?
Anything from laying you back so you can't move, to out of body experiences, amnesia and violent vomiting.

Ketamine

The sensations produced can sometimes be shared by a group of users. A very small amount can produce strong effects. It comes on very powerfully and quickly. Produces a numb sort of feeling. The user's sense of time disappears as it creates the effect of being in a trance for several hours, with pictures sometimes appearing as if a video was being played on the mind.

It is an anaesthetic which was originally produced for animal use. It has also been used during warfare for emergency front line operations.

It can make some people more aggressive.

While it is a wild and overpowering experience, people who are given Ketamine when expecting Ecstacy feel they have been ripped off, probably because you can hardly move, never mind dance. Still, in the right conditions, some really enjoy it.

PRECAUTIONS
Small amounts can be very powerful.

Can immobilise you, so be sure you have a place ready to sit back and watch.

Can cause amnesia, meaning the user may do things they will not remember later so having someone with you to steer you out of trouble is a good idea.

The powder form makes it difficult to know what you're getting, (see Powders page 59).

Things in the *Licence to Trip Test* can apply here, (see page 147).

Government's Opinion
Currently legal as a **prescription** drug, but under review.

Author's Opinion
Someone must have smiled again, so the *kill-joys* are having a look, (see above).

Shame about the soldiers needing Ketamine for emergency surgery, but perhaps if they'd had some before they left, they might have decided not to go out killing people in the first place.

HEAVY!!

PCP

What Is It?
A medical anaesthetic

Other Names:
Angel Dust, Phencyclidine

Where Does It Come From?
Mostly the U.S.A.. It was developed as a veterinary anaesthetic.

What Does It Cost?
From £5 to £15 a dose

What Does It Do?
It stops the body from feeling pain while allowing the user to remain awake. The results can be devastating.

For example, normally when a person tries to lift something heavy, they will stop short of doing any real damage to themselves when they feel the pain of muscles and tendons being torn. On PCP a person will continue to lift *even if the tendons in their arms and legs are being pulled away from the bone!* Such people are very hard to hold down, should they become violent. People have been known to pick up huge appliances, like stoves and even small safes which they repeatedly threw against walls.

PCP

The ability to temporarily bypass the pain signals from the brain gives the user an intense sense of strength which they find enjoyable. Should they try to use this strength, it will indeed be there, but it might take them months recovering from the damage done using it. To make things worse, fits of anger are not uncommon with this drug.

PRECAUTIONS
The powder form this normally comes in makes it difficult to know what you are getting. If you are lucky it will be something else less dangerous, (see Powders page 59).

The risk of loosing control and hurting yourself is great as you probably won't feel the damage done till much much later.

Not recommended for people with poor heart conditions.

(see Serious Health Warnings page 35)

Government's Opinion
It is Class A Illegal (see section on Drug Classes page 31)

Author's Opinion
Not a popular drug in the U.K. and definitely not worth going out to look for.

ANABOLIC STEROIDS

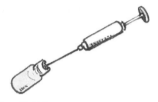

What Is It?
Steroid: any of a group of organic compounds with a characteristic structure of four rings of carbon atoms, including many hormones alkaloids and vitamins.

Anabolic Steroids: any of a group of synthetic steroids used to increase muscle size, (as defined by the Concise Oxford Dictionary).

Other Names:
Nandrolones (Decadurabolin), Halotestin, Phenpropionates, Undanoates, Oxymetholine Anadiol - 50, Mexican Primobolam, Primobolin, Equipoise, Dromostanolone, Winstrol, Oxandrolone, Testosterone undecanoate, Adriol Pantestone, Boldenone Undecylenate, Testosterone suspension, Sustenson 250, Theramex, Sten, Cypionate, Testosterone propionate, Trenbolones, Parabolon, Finajet, Dianebol (methendrostenotone) and more.

Anabolic Steroids

What Does It Cost?
£15 for a months supply to £3000 for a fifteen week course. The wide variety available and varying quality accounts for this huge price spread.

Where Does It Come From?
Spain, Mexico, Russia, Eastern block countries, U.S.A.. Steroids were originally developed for veterinary purposes to make livestock grow bigger.

They were first noted being used by athletes during the 1952 Olympics, by weight lifters. Their popularity has since spread to include most sporting events, which now forbid their use in major competitions. Athletes can be randomly tested and disqualified if found positive. There are still many who feel this risk is worth taking as news reports on positive tests continue to show.

What Does It Do?
Anabolic Steroids encourage muscle growth in the user by providing the body with a new and different set of building instructions. Normally the body uses it's built in set of instructions to replace cells and build muscles as they are needed.

The new and different system provided by the taking of Anabolic Steroids is faster and uses a different pattern for building. The result is that muscles grow bigger and faster with exercise.

This Book

On the down side, as soon as the user stops taking Steroids the natural pattern of the body sets to work unbuilding what has been artificially created. The body sees this different system of building as alien to itself and proceeds to eliminate *all* this new and foreign structure.

While the object of taking Steroids was to get bigger, upon stopping the user will get smaller muscles and will probably become fatter in the process.

Where an athlete might find it useful to have that extra bit of strength on a vital competition day, (if they don't end up being tested), there is no point in using Steroids for any lasting changes, as the constant use needed to maintain those changes poses a serious hazard to the user's health.

Steroids produce their own Testosterones which act in the body to maintain characteristics in males. While the user provides these artificially, the body can see no need to produce it's own. Once the user stops using Steroids, it takes time for the body to resume normal production, and during that time gap depression and feeling weak is common.

Some people suffer more serious side effects and some don't. This is because, given a new set of building instructions the work will begin on the most available area, and there is no way to determine where that will be; so the user seeking larger muscles might end up with larger breasts instead.

Once they stop using this drug the process will reverse as the body reclaims it's territory, but this might take some time.

There are a large number of different types of Anabolic Steroids. Some are moderately safe, while others are out and out dangerous. For instance, if the Steroid is prone to decide the best place to start it's new program of building is your liver or your spleen, you could end up with blood filled cysts from which some people have died.

Apart from muscle building, Anabolic Steroids are used as treatment for bone and muscle disorders and several types of cancer. They are also prescribed to AIDS patients to help revive their appetite.

What follows is a listing of some of the major Anabolic Steroids available and the possible effects of each, which can vary from user to user.

Nandrolones (Decadurabolin) This is a relatively safe injectable when properly used. Can cause zits in younger users, high blood pressure and minor fluctuations in the users sex drive. Not recommended for women.

Anadrol-50 This is very potent and toxic. It can cause liver problems such as peliosis hepatitis which is blood filled cysts which can also occur on the spleen and be life threatening.

Anabolic Steroids

This is a popular oral steroid which some athletes can tolerate for a month, from which they may experience liver pain and increased aggression. Longer use may produce women type breasts on men, hair loss and spots.

Halotestin This has been described as one of the most potentially dangerous of all anabolic agents, but contains no warning on the packet because it is technically an androgen and not an anabolic steroid.

Primobolam This is considered a safe injectable at doses up to 200mg per week. It is reasonably safe for women but can be slightly liver toxic. It is also available in oral form.

Dromostanolone A relatively safe injectable available in 100mg ampoules.

Winstrol *(of Ben Johnson fame)* Available in 2mg tablets or 50mg liquid. Slightly liver toxic; more so in oral form. 150mg - 200mg per week can be used for a short time with no side effects. Higher doses can cause problems in the liver.

Oxandrolone Oral at 15mg a day it is not known to cause any problems to men, but is not recommended for women. Higher doses can cause liver damage as it is slightly liver toxic .

Testosterone undecanoate Adriol Pantestone This is a relatively new product which eliminates most but not all side effects of testosterones. Can be used by women in small doses. Can cause hair loss, acne and bad temper in some users.

Boldenone Undecylenate Equpoise Boldene In doses up to 200mg per week this can produce good muscle gains without great problems for men, but can be a problem for women aromatizing to female hormones. Can unbalance the natural level of sex hormones.

Restosterone Suspension This can cause hair loss, bad temper, high blood pressure, impotence and water retention

Sustenson 250, Theramex
Sten, Cypionate
Testosterone propionate, and Enanthate
These are less toxic to testosterones. Users find these tolerable in doses up to 300mg per week for one month. More than this can cause men to develop women's breast, hair loss and bad temper. In excess of ten weeks on the lower dosage of 300mg per week these can cause hair loss and loss of sex drive.

Trenbolones Only slightly toxic to the liver but this can cause psychological problems such as paranoia, insomnia, nightmares to *full blown psychotic behaviour.*

Anabolic Steroids

Parabolan This is a brand of trenbolones available in 76mg ampoules which are recommended for use no more than once every two weeks, but even at this level the above mentioned problems with trenbolones can occur. It is not otherwise toxic.

Finajet This is a veterinary trenbolone which should be avoided. It is known to cause peliosis hepatitis and temporary insanity. This was never intended for human use.

Equipoise Another veterinary steroid which can cause serious psychotic problems, (roid rage, which is a complete loss of control in a violent temper).

Dianebol (methandrostenolon) This not considered safe and can cause liver damage and roid rage.

Owing to constant new developments, this list can never be complete. You do however have a wide enough range here to give you a good idea of the variety of types these drugs can come in and what they do.

PRECAUTIONS
Nandrolones Anyone using them for 8 weeks or more should have their testosterone level checked by a doctor and also have their high density lipoprotein level checked. It is advisable to use **Nolvadex** or detoxifiers such as **Liv 52** to prevent the build up of too much testosterone and androgens.

Steroids should never be taken for longer periods than what each course recommends.

They can cause some men to become impotent, cause hair loss, growth of women type breast, and acne.

Over use can result in severe liver and spleen damage which might include the growth of blood filled cysts which can be fatal. **If you experience any side effects. stop taking immediately.** There is no way to determine if this might happen in advance.

Most are *not suitable* for women, (check instructions on packs carefully). Women should not use Nandrolones as their mild virilising effects are not reversible.

Most of what is sold as steroids on the black market are fake, so extreme care needs to be taken and purchases made only from someone you can trust. There is now questionable purity from underground laboratories and foreign sources, which is not a problem with those produced legally.

If injecting, never share needles to avoid the spread of diseases.

Those with cholesterol problems should avoid steroids.

Not recommended for people with high blood pressure.
(see Serious Health Warnings page 35)

Anabolic Steroids

Government's Opinion
It is not illegal to possess them, They are controlled under the **prescriptions only** medicines act (1968).

Author's Opinion
When we consider that Steroids work by giving the body a new set of building instructions and that these new plans will be overruled by the body's natural plan once you stop taking them, it makes the whole idea of using Steroids a bit pointless, unless you require that change for only a short or specific time.

You need to ask yourself, are the health risks involved worth taking for the temporary gain these can produce?

If you are an athlete who wants to be in top form on one special day, then you might think, yes it is worth the risk, but even if no side effects occur, you might still loose it all if you end up being tested and disqualified. According to the rules of most sports, using Steroids is considered cheating, giving an unfair advantage.

Maybe in the future we will have completely safe Steroids and the Steroid Olympics. As for today, all are agreed, the best way to make real lasting gains is through a programme of proper exercise and good diet.

IBOGAINE

What Is It?

The root of a shrub taken orally in raw form or in extract purified form.

Other Names:

Ibogaine Hydro Chloride , tabernanthe iboga, Wonder Drug, Endabuse treatment

Where Does It Come From?

Extracted from several plant species native to the rainforest of Central West Africa, it was discovered by botanists in the 1860's, abundant in Gabon. In 1962 a heroin addict named Howard Lotsof found to his surprise that after taking Ibogaine *just once* he no longer was addicted and was able to stop taking heroin with none of the usual bad side effects or cravings.

Ibogaine

What Does It Cost?

One time treatment at the Clinica Hospital America in Panama costs $1500.00 US , about £700. while University of Miami neuro-pathologist Dr Deborah Mash has established a competing 14-day programme in St Kitts (£6,000). Also a devout ibogaine advocate, Eric Taub used to treat people on a boat in international waters. He now has clinics in Costa Rica and Italy at about (£1,000), and is the source of most satisfied experience reports.

What Does It Do?

For thousands of years the Gabonese Bwiti native society have chewed the root of the tabernanthe iboga plant to induce hallucinations in their ancient rights of passage rituals.

This is not a party drug. Users float into a dream state which is best enjoyed sitting or lying down. The strongest part of the trip lasts about 4 hours with effects still being experienced after 7 to 10 hours.

It affects the cerebella part of the brain which is used for learning. People given a test dose of the drug have been able to balance and react as well as those not on the drug, but users would rather not stand or walk when given the choice.

A dream state is induced which seems to give the user a clear view of their life.

Ibogaine

It makes clear the important choices they need to make. People addicted on a drug, such as Heroin, Cocaine, Methadone, Crack and even tobacco, are said to see clearly how the drug is affecting their lives and a strong message is conveyed to encourage them to stop taking the addictive drug.

As if some sort of positive deal has been made, when the addict decides to quit, they suffer none of the expected withdrawals.

Clinical tests have reported a 70% success rate in treating addiction with Ibogaine.

During the trip, users can carry on a conversation and clearly describe to someone else the things they are seeing and feeling.

User Quotes while actually on Ibogaine. "It's like being dead and coming back to life again". "I see a winding movie of my life and it's telling me all these things about it. I re-experience an argument with my mother and realised there was no need for it". "An intense good feeling with everything coming at you, my head is full of amazing information." Things are moving on the walls."

Users have even reported seeing angels guiding them.

A small percentage have what could be described as a bad trip finding it difficult to face the drugs revelations.

It is administered orally, is non addictive, needs a single administration, eliminates narcotic withdrawal, interrupts drug craving, and is effective for extended periods most often indefinitely.

How it affects the attitude of addicts towards drugs and blocks the desire to take them is not fully understood and is currently being studied by the American Food and Drug Administration FDA who have recently approved Ibogaine testing on humans.

As stated in the London Times by Simon Witter "Initial, over-simplified reports of the way ibogaine works suggest-ed that the subject re-lives their entire childhood in 36 hours, during which they identify the holes they are filling with their addictive behaviour. Having understood why they're behaving this way, they wake up cured of those urges. If one dose of ibogaine really did deliver a lifetime of therapy, it would be quite simply the greatest pharma-ceutical breakthrough of the late 20th century - curing all addictions, and thereby not only freeing up all the millions tied up in fruitless drug wars, but also putting therapists all over the planet out of work."

In the early part of the 1900's french scientist first purified the root extract and began doing experiments on animals. In the 1950's the CIA funded secret experiments on humans in the Federal Narcotics Hospital of Lexington in Kentucky.

Ibogaine

Letters written by Harris Isbell, director of the CIA funded project reveal that tests were done on unsuspecting black morphine addicts, but true to government form, the results of the tests he refers to have vanished!

Howard Lotsof, the first modern day addict to experience Ibogaine's cleansing effects has now patented his own Ibogaine treatment called Endabuse in Holland but cannot find the funding needed to satisfy the FDA requirements to make the drug available on prescription to help addicts in the U.S.A.. He points out that the US government would rather spend 300 million dollars on studying cocaine vaccines and antagonists that might block the action of cocaine instead of the mere 10 million he needs to get FDA approval for Ibogaine.

It has also been reported that a Mexican clinic recently refused to carry out Ibogaine research for fear that it would provoke the wrath of local drug lords. Unlike with other important medical discoveries, the development of Ibogaine is being hampered on every level.

One of many theories about why this has happened is that there is a "methadone mafia" entrenched in the scientific/medical community that feels deeply threatened by the prospect of a proper cure to addiction. Whatever the real reason is, Ibogaine's healing properties can only be safely enjoyed clinically at high cost in remote places where the treatment is approved.

Otherwise it's do it yourself. Howard Lotsof says "It makes you wonder".

PRECAUTIONS

Must only be taken in a controlled surrounding and best with a friend there to look after you.

This is not a party drug but more an interspective journey drug, taking you inside yourself to view your life up to now, so be comfortable, ready and relaxed.

Precautions in the licence to trip apply here. It starts on page 147 so have a look if you haven't already, and be sure you understand it before even considering Ibogaine.

Currently available as a medical treatment in the Clinica Hospital America in Panama where, if you can afford it, you will be in safe hands, but you might end up with all sorts of probes and wires connected to you, so valuable research can be done while you are on your journey.

If taken in powder form it is difficult to know for sure what or how much it is you are taking. As we know, powders are often mixed with undesirable other things by dealers wishing to make a higher profit. (see Powders for fuller explanation, page 59).

There is a danger of death from overdose.
(see section on Serious Health Warnings, page 35)

Ibogaine

Governments Opinion:
While it is legal everywhere else, Ibogaine is restricted in Belgium and Switzerland and illegal in the US where, ironically, it is classed in the same category as the hard drugs from which it provides relief (a result of the panicky, post-psychedelia 1970 Controlled Substances act.)

Author's Opinion
It does indeed make you wonder. A drug with the ability to help addicts to beat addiction, known of by the U.S. government since the 1950's, and still finding it impossible to get research funding?

It would seem to works in a very psychological and almost spiritual way by giving the person a positive view of their life which, once seen, makes it easy to make the best most healthy choice, even eliminating the need for anti-depressants which currently cost the Health Service millions every year. So what's wrong with that?

Maybe it would be too much for the establishment to admit that a psychoactive substance can actually be good for you.

Say it really can cure addiction, then this would also reduce crime, and this would be good, except of course for those who make their living out of dealing with crime, like the law makers, the judges, court bailiffs, solicitors, police, probation, prison governors and warders to name but a few;

not listing their assistants and of course those employed in making all the materials they need, like prisons and wigs and paper clips. Would a cure be suppressed at high level just to keep all these people from losing their jobs?*

Or maybe the heroin trade. which would be the worst to suffer. is *really* run by government agencys using diplomats to move the stuff in their diplomatic pouches, and the CIA convieniently lost the results of the Ibogaine tests when it became clear this drug really works to cure addiction?

Or maybe the scientific/medical community really is threatened by an effective cure for addiction which would make their current expensive and dangerous treatments obsolete, effectively eliminating Methadone deaths.

Or possibly the officials who first saw the test results didn't particularly like drug addicts very much and felt it wasn't worth the bother, or they just didn't care?

Naw, what am I saying? Our beloved governments and the pharmaceutical companies sceaming to keep their jobs, being involved in the drugs trade, or not really caring. How could that possibly be? I really must stop drinking so much coffee.

* *Come to think of it, making drugs legal would have much the same effect.*

Things are looking up!

VIAGARA

What Is It?

It's an anti-impotence drug which is taken orally in tablet form, in doses of 25mg, 50mg or 100mg

Other Names:

Sildenafil

Where Does It Come From?

A drug company called Pfizer in Kent the UK, originally developed it as a treatment for angina, a heart condition. Male patients surprised the company when they reported improved erections after taking it.

What Does It Cost?

Between £4 and £5 on the NHS, £15 private and up to £40 on the black market for one dose.

What Does It Do?

It is taken by men who have problems getting or maintaining an erection.

It works by causing smooth muscle relaxation in the penis which then allows the inflow of blood needed to cause and maintain an erection.

Viagra

The area affected is the *corpus cavernosum*, (for those of you who like technical names).

It needs to be taken about an hour before intercourse, so you need to plan your spontainious moves carefully. Sexual stimulation is still required to produce the desired effect, so no worries about an embarrassing bulge appearing when that late night coffee turns out of be just coffee. Romantics who like to take their time might note that eating food delays the activity.

It is not an addictive drug.

PRECAUTIONS

You really should see a doctor before taking Viagra, as advised in the section on Serious Health Warnings page 35, only this time it's OK to mention what you would like to do, because you can't get arrested for it. (see next section)

Should be avoided by people with high blood pressure, heart disease, diabetes, heart stroke history or hereditary degenerative retinal disorders.

NOT TO BE TAKEN WITH POPPERS! or drugs which contain nitrates. Taking amyl nitrates with Viagra **can be fatal.**

(Amyl nitrates section starts on page 114.)

Some side effects which have been reported are headaches, flushing, dizziness and altered vision. It is therefore not advisable to drive or use machinery after taking Viagra.

(Depression and altered vision are more common at the higher dose of 100mg.)

There have been 69 reported deaths from taking Viagra in the United States since it's licensing (Nov 98), some caused from people not knowing or heeding the precautions above. While the loss these 69 people is a tragedy, it also has to be seen against the back drop of the more than four million prescriptions which have currently been written as we go to press with this second edition.

Government's Opinion
Currently legal with prescription.

Author's Opinion
It's strange how when we look back in history, all the major societies and Empires seemed to believe that they had reached the peak of knowledge and had the answers to all the major questions.

And each new one which comes along is quick to see how limited the previous ones were, while not seeing the limitations they have themselves.

Viagra

Look at us, we travel in space, we have mass media, and enjoy what we dare to call 'advanced medical science', yet somehow it feels to me like we are still very young and only just scratching the surface of what we could be.

For too long we have concentrated our skills on making weapons of mass destruction; and we are forced to pay tax money to help develop what destructive people believe is important, while the creative and the romantic are pushed to one side.

It's good to see scientists working on something which can help people to have normal physical relationships, and it's good to see that intimacy is now beginning to be seen as important instead of obscene.

Isn't it odd that it's fine to show war movies on a Sunday afternoon on TV, with hundreds of soldiers being killed on the screen, but two people making love, well you can't show that, can you? At least not until all the children are asleep.

It's too early for me to really comment on Viagra. These next few years will tell us how good it really is, but I can safely say, the more we concentrate on love and sharing and the less we work on hurting each other, the better off we all will be.

CURIOSITY KILLED THE CAT

Satisfaction brought him back

It is worth restating that it is not *This Book's* intention to encourage anyone to experiment with illegal drugs. This Book's aim is to inform any who are interested in this subject for whatever reason. People read books about motor racing but might never intend to go out on a track with a high powered car.

Curiosity

It's only natural to be curious, that being the only route to discovering new things. And also it is necessary to *really* find out about something before you can sensibly decide for or against.

Our next section is called *Connoisseur's Guide Cannabis Round the World.* It will be valuable to anyone seeking wider knowledge on the subject.

This knowledge might be useful in planning a trip to Amsterdam for instance, or you might baffle your kids by being able to tell them what region that lump of hash you found in their room is from.

Whatever your reason for reading on, I hope you enjoy our World Tour of the Cannabis Community, which is steadily growing larger by the day.

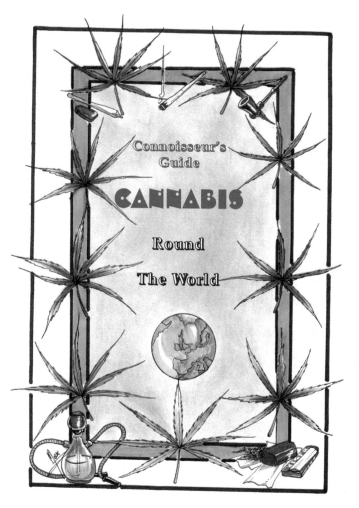

Connoisseur's
Guide

CANNABIS

Round

The World

CONNOISSEUR'S GUIDE
CANNABIS ROUND THE WORLD

My friend Pete tells me that there are two main forms Cannabis can come in, *herbal* or *hash, (Hairy-Mess reminds me that in fact there are three types. We nearly forgot OILs). THANKS HAIRY.*

Herbal is simply the leafy part of the plant dried. It requires no processing whatsoever. Just pick, dry, and consume. It can be smoked or eaten.

Hash itself comes in two main forms - resin or pollen.

Resin is a sticky substance which can be taken off the leaves, and pollen is shaken from the plants over a screen, so the pollen drops to a sheet beneath. It's collected and pressed into tins. A Common mould is one producing the 9 ounce bar which looks like a bar of soap (from which it gets it's name, "Soap"). But it can also come in many other shapes or sizes.

THE GOOD HASH GUIDE

Let's start with a look at one of these soaps on our tour. For this we need to go to Morocco to find some **Double Zero (OO) Rocky**, so called because that is the gauge size of the screen used to sift it. They seem to have it right because this type is very popular.

About 15 years ago all Moroccan Hash was pollen in a light blonde colour. Then some Afghanis revolutionised the production and began making a dark hash, (when fleeing there after the U.S.S.R. invaded Afghanistan). Before this happened, it was a standing joke to refer to Black Moroccan in the presence of a hash novice to see if they would bite and claim to have tried some of that which did not exist. Maybe one of the people caught on that joke was an Afghani who, to get his own back, went to Morocco and changed their process. Probably not.

The bits left over after the pollen and resin has been removed is called **Kif**, which must have some THC left in it because it is sold locally sometimes mixed with tobacco and widely used by people of all ages.

Cannabis is now grown in rotation in Morocco, providing five separate crops per year. One of these crops might produce some **Slate from Ketama** which is a blonder colour than soap. It is pressed much thinner not being as strong as Double Zero (OO), and creating a lighter high.

Connoisseur's Cannabis Guide

The Himalayan Mountains are filled with stories of spiritual lore with legends of long living Gurus and miraculous happenings. This is also the home of some of the world's best hashes. Each hash has it's own special flavour and aroma, and each has its unique way of taking effect.

Nepalese can be found in Buddhist temples being burnt as incense. It is a very strong black hash. To use in the temple, Buddhist Monks roll the hash into balls, (**Temple Balls**), which are generally the size of a football look really rough with bits of twigs, seeds etc. within them. This hash can be mildly hallucinogenic.

Kashmir comes in two forms. One is hard and grey in the form of a twist., (Imagine two finger size pieces twisted together about 6 inches in length). The other comes soft in black greeny blocks. This hash is very pungent and reputed to be one of the strongest in the world. It produces a more spiritual high, (a lighter feeling).

Menali is reported to have the highest THC content of any hash in the world. It is hallucinogenic and has a very fruity smell not unlike oranges.

There are two types of Cannabis from **Hishmal Predash** in the foot hills of the Himalayas. Some is growing wild and some is cultivated. The wild is fruitier and more expensive. Also it wouldn't be right to leave these mountains without mentioning **Kirali.** This is a very strong dark grass.

Connoisseur Cannabis is sponsored by.....
NHS
N.H.S SUPPLIES
NHS Supplies
P.O.BOX 176
BICESTER D.O
OX6 7RD
TEL: 07887 955027
www.herbal-peripherals.co.uk
HEMP TEST KITS.
SEEDS, BOOKS, BONGS, LEGAL STIMULANTS
ALL SEEDS SOLD AS SOUVENIERS ONLY.

India has always been a place of mystery to many in the Western World. Magic carpets and the Indian rope trick come to mind. You know the one where the rope is coaxed into climbing out of the basket into mid air by the sound of a flute so a young boy can climb to the top, only to disappear before your very eyes. Modern day sceptics have said this illusion might be caused by hypnotism. None as far as I know have ever put it down to **Bombay Black**, yet this is considered to be the commercial dope of India, much of which is sold to tourists who end up watching the Indian rope trick; (*another mystery solved perhaps??*) The fact that it is relatively cheap is a bonus.

Charas is the cream of the cream of Indian hashes with the pollen being collected for it's production before the resin is removed from the leaves

Cannabis is rich in lore and history. One story being told is that some Black Hashes are produced by sending naked virgins to run through the fields gathering the resin on their skin, to be later scraped off and rolled on their thighs. Sounds like promotional hype to me, but if anyone knows different, send photos please.

From Pakistan we have a black hash affectionately known as **Paki-Black.** It is a mixture of hash, ghee, or honey. It's form makes it tempting for dealers to break it up and add a filler such as henna, and as a result it is not often found pure in the U.K..

This Book

Some have even been known to add pig tranquillisers to the mixture. It comes sealed in cellophane which can be red, clear or gold. Many people think the colour of seal indicates the quality, but it does not. What colour of seal used is just whatever takes the packer's fancy. It bears no relation to the product. The idea that the colour of the seal means something is a carry over from when all first rate Paki-Black had what looked like a Royal seal of approval imprinted on it. This does not seem to be happening these days.

Hash has been around for a long time, but it was not always called Hash. Leader of an Islamic sect, Hasan-I Salsah in days of old (circa 1092) had a troop of approximately 60 elite soldiers who erected a near impregnable fortress at Alamut in Persia, later expanding to bases in Syira. Their modus operandi was political murder of prominent Muslims.The night before a battle, it was rumoured Hasan-I Salsah would give them a taste of the after life to make them brave and unafraid of death. They would be taken to a secret garden, given a drink made from hash and allowed their way with many beautiful women. While these rumours were never proven beyond doubt historically, they were believed by their opponents who labelled them Assassins, The Hashisheen, and their association with Cannabis gave Hashish it's name. (which we shortened to Hash, because we're like that.)

Afganistan has long been known for it's fine hash. This is a black hash usually thicker pressed than Paki-Black and every bit as strong. All black hashes have their own distinctive characteristics, this being no exception.

The local **Afghan Kabul Hash** produces a "spiritual rather than a splatter high", in the words of a user.

All hashes are capable of producing great guffaws.

The Arab States all produce hash. **Egypt, Syria, Libya,** all have their own, but not much of this reaches the U. K.. You will find some in Holland if you check the coffee shops where you can buy up to 30 grams without fear of prosecution. More on that later.

What we might find in Britain is **Lebanese red or gold,** but a lot of what is sold *as* Lebanese is actually from Syria.

While Lebanese red is dark red and it's gold is light blond, **Syrian hash** looks like the two have been mixed into one, producing an in between shade. It is very pungent and comes in a hessian bag. One would think you empty the bag and throw the hessian away, but if you were lucky enough to find a bag which had been handled in this way, you might discover up to 1/2 ounce of hash tucked into the inside folds of the bag. Sometimes the bags are boiled after use, producing a very enjoyable potent brew.

CANNABIS OIL

Most of the places which produce hash also produce hash oil. This is made by soaking the Cannabis or grass in neat alcohol. After the solids are strained off the liquid is put in a double-boiler to distil it. There was a time when this was extra strong but sadly these days Cannabis oils are often diluted with other oils making them disappointing.

HERBAL CANNABIS

The Good Weed Guide
My friend Clive informs me that **Marijuana** comes in two genetic varieties: *Cannabis Sativa* such as Thai, N. African, S. American, (Mexican and Colombian). And *Cannabis Indica* such as Hindu Kush, (Asian, Indian), Jamaican, Central and Southern Africa.

Cannabis Sativa is a tall wild plant which produces high levels of cannabidinol (CBN) and cannabidolic acid (C.B.D.) and low levels of tetrahydrocannabinol (T. H. C.) which produces a sedative or narcotic effect.

Cannabis Indica is a short, stocky plant which produces higher levels of THC and is therefore more psycho-active. Most forms of Cannabis are cultivated in warmer climates.

This Book

Even in less temperate climates this can be achieved by using black bin liners, placed over the plants to promote early flowering, thereby effectively bringing maturity forward before summer fades away.

Nowadays Cannabis can also be grown indoors, using powerful lamps. This has proven very effective and some of the best Cannabis in the world is now grown in laboratory conditions. Using Metal Halide Lamps, of up to 1000 watts to promote early vegative growth, and High Pressure Sodium Lamps, even more powerful, to promote heavy flowering, indoor growers can produce five crops each year.

With the introduction of *Hydroponics,* (growing without soil), along with carefully calculated bursts of C.O.2, (carbon dioxide), Growers can expect Cannabis up to <u>ten</u> <u>times</u> as potent as their outdoor rivals.

New strains have been hybrid, to compliment the indoor bloom, such as **Skunk, Super Skunk, Northern Lights,** (originally Californian outdoor variety), **Early Girl**, (early flowering), **Silver Haze,** and **Ruderalis Skunk,** (a hybrid of Skunk and a Russian variety which flowers as soon as it roots). These are generally grown for Sensi-milia (seedless which is a female plant removed from the males early on, to avoid pollination. This encourages the female flowers to produce more cannabidinols, such as THC, in an attempt to attract the pollen of the removed plants). These flowers are cut when mature, hung upside down to dry, then trimmed and cured making them ready to smoke.

251

Cannabis is produced in all parts of Africa. All the Arab and Hindu nations produce hash, where as the African black nations produce grass almost without exception, which is an interesting and unexplained phenomena. They call grass *Dagga* in S. Africa.

Some of the best African grasses include South African known as **Durban Poison.** This is a straw green colour, where as what is sold more commercially is darker green. It is sticky and smells of ammonia. Dutch immigrants cultivate most of this, (an absolute must for the discerning doobie-head).

One of the best grasses is probably **Malawi,** grown in the area surrounding Nyasa, which comes in cobs, which some claim have been buried for months to mature it. It has lovely light green buds simular to outdoor Skunk, (see Skunk page 242), which are well cultivated by proud farmers. It has recently increased in interest owing to it's breeding potential.

Grass in general produces a more giggly high, less heavy thinking and more jolly.

Grass is a very important part of the Rastafarian religion (of which Bob Marley was probably it's most famous follower). I will not attempt to describe all that these people believe, because that would merit a separate book. But one part of their belief does puts God in an interesting light.

Genesis chapter 1 verses 11 and 12

Connoisseur's Cannabis Guide

Take a quick look at the beginning of the Bible and you'll find that the first organic substance to be mentioned in the Genesis story of Creation is, you guessed it, *GRASS*.

Here is the full quote most commonly referred to:

11) Then God said "Let the earth bring forth grass, the herb that yields seed, and the fruit tree that yields fruit according to it's kind, whose seed is in itself, on the earth," and it was so.

12) And the earth brought forth grass, the herb that yields seed according to it's kind, and the tree that yields fruit whose seed is in itself according to it's kind. And God saw that it was good.

Genesis chapter one,
Verses 11 and 12
The New King James Version
of The Holy Bible

I mentioned this fact to MAX while he was busy creating some of the cartoon characters for This Book and he immediately stopped what he was doing to catch the inspiration of what that moment might have been like when God created grass and saw that it was good,

(it has been argued that the only way to really know for sure if grass is good or not is to try it)

This Book

Personally I don't imagine God with a long beard sitting on a throne, but I do see how grass is a natural part of Creation, and I can see why the Rastas quote these verses.

In the **Caribbean** each region's grass varies slightly and has different properties.

Columbia is a huge producer of grass and has in the region of two dozen types. These all vary in strength and in appearance. **Chiba** for instance can come in black, red, green or gold. The commercial grasses go from good to seedy.

Santa Mata is not as good as Chiba. It comes in **red or gold**. It is however better than commercial.

In Mexico we find **Accapolco Gold.** It is rumoured that a tobacco company has registered Accapolco Gold as a trade mark, ready for Cannabis' legalisation. This grass, as you might guess is a goldy colour. When well tended this is a prime sativa. It is not as strong as Colombian grasses, but it is known to produce a nice happy high which is why it is so popular.

Panama Red runs neck in neck with Accapolco Gold and it is the flip of a coin which is best loved. It's colour lives up to it's name.

Connoisseur's Cannabis Guide

In California we find **Sensi-milia** a grass with seedless buds. This is a hybrid grown plant which has been developed through careful cross-pollination, which has become an art in itself.

One masterpiece is known as **California Northern Lights**, which is number one in many people's books. This is a hybrid from Hawaiian and Jamaican. Producing small compact plants with heavy flowering. It is sticky, aromatic and almost completely covered in a frosty coating which reflects in the light. Here we also find **Cali red beard,** a sensi-milia with characteristic red hairs on the tips. It is very sticky and strong.

In Thailand we find what many feel is the best foreign grass to be found in the U.K.. This comes in **Thai Sticks**. They look like grass leaves twisted onto a thin stick about six inches long and tied on with thread. You unravel the thread carefully to use the grass. It is a very respectable classic Sativa, although suspected to have had it's hey day, due to supply and demand making it not as popular now. As a rule, the more remote the source, the better the crop. these days you might even find that your Thai Stick has actually come from Cambodia or Laos.

In fact excellent grass is produced in all the neighbouring countries, including **Cambodia, Vietnam, and Laos,** which owes a lot to the warm and suitable climate for it's fine selection.

256

We also have grass from Morocco, often referred to as **African Bush,** because of it's twiggy uncultivated appearance. This classic old sativa has fallen from grace since the hashish boom in the 60's, when demand began to outweigh supply. This has lead to the downfall of the small dedicated farmer.

Congolese is grown in the Congo Basin. This fine well preserved weed produces tight sticky buds which rarely find their way out of Africa. It can be described as satisfying and mellow, yet still potent.

Nigerian is twiggy, seedy and over produced, being very bushy and wild. You always seem to throw too much away, but it still does the job.

Ruderalis is short, spiky Russian weed low in THC, but recently hybrid with Skunk to create an early flowering potent grass which, if grown indoors, can reach full maturity in as little as 45 days.

Lebanese is almost exclusively grown these days for hashish export, but there are still some rare stashes to be found, well worth looking for.

Hindu Kush (Ancient Indica) is still widely in use for Hashish and Marijuana all over the Himalayas, Afghanistan and Northern India, being short stocky plants, dark with a definitive purple leaf which is very resinous.

Southern Indian. This region produces some of the finest examples of weed ever produced out of doors, with a reliable taste and high.

Manilla (Vanilla, Phillipines) is the home of some fine plantations growing this light golden bud, perhaps well known owing to it's position in all the major fishing lanes, providing it with easy transport.

Cannabis Americana is grown in impressive examples all over Kentucky and most other southern American states from east to west coast. This is also the home of the *"Furry Freak Brothers"*, whose famous motto is *"Dope will get you through times of no money better than money getting you through times of no dope."* This marijuana loving trio are the stars of some of the most successful underground comic books ever made. Those familiar with Fat Freddy will know he would be partial to a bit of Hawaiian (**Maui Wowie**) which is frosty with green, orange and purple flowers. Excellent sensi-milia high in THC.

Jamaican: Small well run farms produce the finest Jamaican **Kali Weed,** and some splendid Indica-based sensi-milia in fact this was the place that gave the name Sensi-milia (seedless) to the world. It is short, dark and very pungent, fairly high (up to 10%) in THC.

Skunk: Originally meaning "homegrown" in dutch, now it is the name of the fast growing new hybrid, coming from

Holland and containing some Sativa parentage such as Thai, and some Indica such as Hindu Kush. Indoors or out this is a must for the grower, producing high yields and record THC levels. Now grown all over Europe, and being threatened with "A" classification, this is a serious step forward for compact and discrete farming.

Shiva Shanti: Simular to skunk, but not as potent, this is a good place to start learning to grow, as it is a very easily cultivated plant for outdoors even in Europe.

Silver Haze is another good hybrid along with **Early Girl**, both named appropriately.

SuperSkunk is a variation of skunk believed to be secretly crossed with the hop plant, to produce bigger, heavier flowers of the same quality as Skunk.

Northern Lights Number 5- Haze is of course a cross breed which has been winning all the big prizes at the weed festivals, but quality seems to replace quantity, with smaller yields of a much higher potency.

Australia is also producing some exciting new breeds, all from imported parentage, and some fine purple heads have been spotted in **New Zealand.**

This Book

Generally speaking there are people growing Cannabis in practically *every* country in the world. What we have here is a sort of cultural revolution involving millions of people who have decided that their governments are wrong, at least on this one issue.

Some countries have begun to see how wide spread Cannabis' popularity is, and have begun to tolerate it's use.

In Amsterdam as in many other Dutch cities and towns, up to thirty grams can be bought or sold without fear of prosecution and this is done openly in Coffee Shops. There are hundreds of these shops.

In Holland they have decided to separate Cannabis from other drugs. They feel what makes some people go from Cannabis onto 'hard' drugs is mostly the fact that these are sold by the same person. So they allow coffee shops to sell up to thirty grams without any bother. There's no point in a Heroin dealer selling grass now, which anyone can buy openly, and the grass smoker is never offered anything stronger than coffee.

There are some very impressive statistics to show how this approach works really well, (*Heroin use is reported to have gone down considerably*).

From the user's point of view it is very relaxed place to smoke with a very wide variety of hashes and grass to choose from. Most coffee shops have a menu with about twenty choices and some include samples to let the connoisseur see what they're buying, with some shops specialising in regional types.

The Dutch approach appears to be more honest when you consider that no major drug has ever been eradicated by legislation once it has infiltrated a community.

As you will see from the extent and variety of Cannabis produced, it is not about to go away.

I hope you found our tour of *Cannabis Round the World* interesting, but our Connoisseur's Guide would not be complete without a look at how people who would rather not smoke can enjoy hash and grass. What follows are some recipe ideas from our Gourmet of the Ganja Chef Jaycee.

A closing thought: If people could buy Cannabis from the same counter as where they find Alcohol, many would do so, and considering it's relaxing effects this would probably lead to less violent crimes being committed.

GOURMET
GANJA
RECIPE
IDEAS

HASH BROWNIES

You'll need:
One box of chocolate cake mix
1/8 ounce of hash or grass (Slab Rocky is ideal)
One caramel icing mix
Butter

Preparation
Holding a flame to a piece of hash, crumble into melted butter until it dissolves then mix into the cake mix, like one would into a joint.
Bake as usual at gas mark four.

This Book

Caution:
Open the window while baking (why?, unless you want every one to know what you're up to) and guard the bowl from eager lickers.

With baking completed, remove from oven and allow to cool before applying caramel icing which brings out the taste in the hash really well.

Cut into two inch squares.

Eat three of those and you won't be doing much for the rest of the day. It is a much much more intense high than from smoking.

Often these cakes don't make it to the table, being eaten on the way.

Note: Some mixes come with paper trays which create ideal portions.

You can be imaginative with cakes, using grass in the cake and hash in the icing, with a bit of hash to decorate the top.

BOMBAY VEGETABLE CURRY

(serves two to four)

You'll need:
One half pound each of assorted vegetables, including;
carrots, mushrooms, potatoes, celery, green peppers,
onions, etc.
1/4 pound of raisins
Some incense
Curry powder or a can of curry sauce
One cup of rice (brown or white)
1/2 oz of fine grass or hash (Rocky Slab is ideal)
Olive oil

Preparation

Dice your vegetables, place in a pot and cover with water.
Bring to the boil.

Drop back heat to simmer and add your curry powder or premix to taste.

Leave to simmer for 45 minutes, stirring occasionally to prevent sticking.

Start your rice in boiling water (as per instructions on the pack).

Again heat your hash over a flame and crumble into hot olive oil until it melts then add in the final five minutes of cooking, or if you're using grass, sprinkle on just before serving.

Be careful not to over cook or you'll cook out the goodness.

If you have both hash and grass add in proportion as suggested above.

Add your raisins.

Drain the rice when cooked, add to plates, topping with your sauce.

Light your incense, turn down the lights and eat cross legged on the floor, to be really authentic use your fingers and chant.

COSMIC BOLOGNESE

(serves two to four)

You'll need:

One pound of bolognese style beef or soya/tofu
One tin of tomato paste
One tin of tomatoes
One tin of tomato soup
1/2 lb of mushrooms, normal (optional)
One green pepper
One large onion
Mixed herbs
1/8 oz of fine grass or hash
Cooking oil
Salt
Two cups of pasta - your choice

Preparation

Finely chop the green pepper and onion.

Finely slice the mushrooms.

Add a thin layer of cooking oil to the bottom of the frying pan and fry the vegetables together (you may add garlic if you like).

Mix the tomato paste with the tinned tomatoes and the tomato soup in a large bowl.

Add one cup of water and a pinch of mixed herbs.

With onions green pepper and mushrooms frying well, add your tomato mixture and turn down to simmer.

Prepare a pot of boiling water with one teaspoon of salt and add your pasta (see instructions on pack).

While your sauce is simmering add soya/tofu or ground beef.

Prepare your grass, making sure it is clean of seeds and stems.

At a late stage in the cooking when the sauce is fine to your taste, add the grass and allow to simmer for five minutes only.

Drain pasta when cooked and place servings on plates.

Add your sauce individually to each serving.

Eat and don't expect to do the dishes until the next day.

STEW YOU

(Serves two to four)

You'll need:

1/8 lb each of various vegetables. Go to your green grocer and be creative.

1/2 cup of lentils

1 stock cube (veg or meat)

One large onion

Cooking oil

Salt

Mixed herbs

One glass of wine (or a can of beer)

1/2 ounce of hash or grass (again Slab Rocky is best but any good hash will do)

Preparation

Thinly dice your onion.

Add cooking oil to the frying pan and lightly fry the diced onion adding mixed herbs to taste.

Thickly dice your vegetables and place in a pot on a stove.

Cover with boiling water, add salt to taste and sprinkle in your stock cube.

Let simmer for ten minutes.

Add your lentils

While simmering add your fried onions stirring occasionally.

You'll need to wait about 45 minutes before adding the hash in the same way described for the curry, so you can take a break now and drink the wine or/and beer.

After 45 minutes add the hash or grass during the last five minutes of cooking, serve in big bowls and eat with wooden spoons if you have any.

GRASS HIGH TEA

Grass tea can be made from the stalks of plants which are not much use for smoking but do contain enough THC to make it a pleasurable drink.

For one large pot you'll need the stocks from three or four small plants.

Use as tea leaves and add boiling water.
Tea's Up!

HASH COFFEE

Melt crumbled hash in spirit (Amarreto is recommended) and mix it with hot milk, sugar/honey and coffee using about 1/8 oz in a pot for a fine result.

This Book

These are just a few ideas you can use to celebrate on the day they legalise cannabis, when it comes.

So ends our Connoisseur's Guide to Cannabis Round the World. I'm sure you'll agree we've explored a wide variety and many uses. If however, your favourite has been missed, or you have some unusual cooking ideas, drop us a line and we might include them in our next edition with special thanks to you. You'll find the address for Those Publishers at the start of This Book. I'm always interested in hearing new creative ideas about anything you feel is good, so don't hesitate to write if you have anything you'd like to share.

A BRIEF HISTORY OF DRUGS

Did you know that Cannabis has been around so long that it was probably once munched on by dinosaurs?

Around 5000 B.C., as soon as people could write, the Sumerians were relating the joys of Opium.

In Egypt about 3500 B.C., on papyrus paper we find the first recorded use of Alcohol.

Around 2500 B.C. it is recorded that lake dwellers in Switzerland were eating poppy seeds.

For thousands of years North and South American Indians have been using psychedelic plants which contained Mescaline, D.M.T. and other less known psychoactive elements to aid them in spiritual experiences

Since 2500 B.C. native Altiplano Indians in South America have been chewing the leaves of the Coca plant to help them work long hours.

About 1000BC- The completed Indian mythology Vedas calls Marijuana a gift from the gods for curing many minor ills, lowering fevers, improving judgement by quickening the mind and curing sleeplessness. (called Soma)

A Brief History Of Drugs

30 A.D., Christ's first recorded miracle was turning water into wine.

In 1493 Columbus discovered the Indians of North America smoking what they called sacred tobacco.

On his next voyage, Columbus reports on the natives use of D.M.T. in 1496.
(Could it be that he got stoned on some plants containing D.M.T. and got conned into taking ordinary tobacco instead of the sacred tobacco which the Indians used in the pipe of peace? Of course when he got back, as the theory goes he could hardly admit to his mistake so he convinced the Old World people to smoke it anyway, they gave it half a chance, most of them got hooked and old Columbus had a ready market for what the Indians considered to be crap. Enter Sir Walter Raleigh. That's one idea that's been put forward which I though you might find amusing. What we do know is that Columbus was a drug importer, what we don't know for sure is whether he was ripped off or not).

1750 we find Coca leaves being imported into Europe as a health giving tonic with unusual powers.

In 1844 Cocaine was isolated into it's pure form.

In the mid 1800's Amyl Nitrate was used as a cure for Angina, also Cannabis is being used widely as cure for headaches and insomnia.

1839-1860: Britain fought two wars against China to force the Chinese government to accept the importation of Opium from it's colony India. At this time Opium is widely available in shops across the U.K..

1864 is when the first Barbiturates were produced.

1868: Dr George Wood, author of a major textbook 'Treatise on Therapeutics' wrote of Opium; "The intellectual and imaginative faculties are raised to the highest point compatible with individual capacity. . . it seems to make the individual, for a time, a better and greater man."

1884: Sigmund Freud first used Cocaine and praised it as a magnificent substance.

1885: John Pemberton produced a product called "French Wine of Coca, Ideal Tonic". A year later, enhanced by Kola Nut and extra syrup it became known as Coca-Cola.

1887: Amphetamines were first synthesised in Germany.

1898: We find Heroin being produced from Morphine.

1903: Caffeine was substituted for Cocaine in Coca-Cola. A subsequent law suit to try and force Coca-Cola to change it's name because it no longer contained Coca failed because it was ruled Coca-Cola was now a household name.

A Brief History Of Drugs

Between 1870 and 1915 tax on alcoholic liquor provided
1/2 to 2/3 of the entire tax revenue in the U.S.A..

In 1909 the United States prohibited the importation of
Opium.

In 1910 MDA was first produced in Europe.

In 1916 U.S. Department of Agriculture scientists devised
a method of making paper from hemp (cannabis) pulp
which, if used widely, would make wood pulp paper making obsolete. (Cannabis needs no pesticides and is much
more economical to grow than trees or cotton providing a
yearly harvest and producing a better product.)

1919: Alcohol was banned in the U.S.A.. This was called
prohibition.

From 1920 the Hurst News Empire is campaigning heavily
against Cannabis. Hurst has huge investments tied up in
wood pulp making

1920: Cocaine becomes illegal in the U.K..

1924: Cannabis becomes illegal in the U.K.. 1924 Up until
this time the Encyclopedia Brittanica estimates there was a
regular use of Cannabis by more than 300,000,000 people
as a cure for many ills from tetanus to hydrophobia.

By 1928 the medical profession was earning an estimated 40 million dollars a year prescribing whisky!

In 1933 prohibition ended with many people saying "I'll drink to that.".

In April 1943 a Swiss chemist, Albert Hoffman accidentally ingested 250 micro grams of LSD and had the first Acid Trip.

1952: The Olympics see the introduction of Steroids.

1953: Sir Winston Churchill makes his rousing speech to the Tory Party Conference in Margate, while high on amphetamines, (his doctor has since revealed).

In the early 1960s Dr. Timothy Leary coined the phrase "Turn on, tune in, drop out." a reference to taking LSD.

From the early '60s to 1985 ecstasy (MDMA) was available legally in clubs across the U.S.A..

In 1964 Amphetamines were outlawed in the U.K..

1966: LSD was made illegal in the U.K.

1985: MDMA became illegal in the USA.

Every year cigarettes kill more Americans than were killed in World War II, The Korean and Vietnam war combined.

Drugs? What Drugs?

PRISON AND DRUGS

As we look around us at the way things are, it's easy to get the impression that things have always been this way.

Strange to think that 85 years ago there was not a single person being kept in prison for a drugs offense. It's not like drugs have just arrived creating the need to ban them. As you will have seen from our brief history of drugs many of these substances have been around for thousands of years.

What happened was that a short while back a small group of people fell under a false impression, thinking that if they banned something it would eliminate that thing from society. This approach has never worked. Far from eliminating, banning has only served to make the thing more popular, giving it a mystique and a high profit value.

Prison and Drugs

One would think that when something proves to have the opposite effect to that intended, this would be sound grounds for rethinking the idea. But, instead of having a fresh look, our present leaders choose to invest more and more into a failing plan.

As a result, a fortune is being spent on keeping people convicted of drug offenses in prison, while the drug trade goes from strength to strength.

But what of those who have been convicted and find themselves behind bars? One would at least think that this severe punishment would convince them not to be involved with drugs anymore. Funnily enough the opposite is true.

It is very difficult to find a prisoner who doesn't take some illegal drug or other and drugs are freely traded for phone cards and tobacco every single day of the week behind bars.

Many prison officers have admitted to me that the smoking of Cannabis keeps a prison quiet, and some inmates feel being stoned is the only way to do their time.

Prisoners, like many others in society realise that the drug laws are unworkable and ineffective.

If all drugs were made legal today it would be the drug dealers who would be crying the loudest.

They would effectively be put out of business overnight.

As a society we could subject producers to quality control tests, providing a "Seal of Approval" to only the purest products, making drugs without that seal less desirable and unsellable. Random tests with the threat of the seal's withdrawal for sub-standard goods would keep the producers on their toes and have them competing with each other to get the highest grade.

Our Mass Media could be effectively used to black list any products which were found to be impure or dangerous. With this method we could eliminate all the problems related to contaminated products.

With a bit of honest education instead of hypocritical legislation we could encourage more common sense concerning the use of drugs. Perhaps "This Book" could be of use towards that end.

No-one can say that we didn't give the idea of banning drugs a fair try, and no-one can say that it's working. Sensible people do not carry on supporting methods which are obviously failing.

Putting people in prison for drug offenses is not a working policy, it's more like a vindictive attack on people for having a different life style. It's almost seems like they are jealous of young people enjoying themselves. It's time this pointless exercise came to an end.

283

Prison and Drugs

Under our present so called democratic system one might complain that no decent alternative is being offered to vote for. If no decent alternative is being put forward then perhaps it's time to seriously consider putting one forward ourselves.

Our present leaders do not believe that we are capable of presenting and electing our own representatives.

They do not believe we are capable of abandoning old failing ideas and adopting new workable ones.

They rely on people who don't vote to continue not voting so they can carry on ruling with the support of the minority that does vote for them.

(If you add up the number of people who voted for other parties with the number of people who didn't vote, the number is almost always larger than the number of votes polled by the winning party).

Apart from persecuting people with different lifestyles, our present members of parliament have an attitude which is very destructive to life on our planet and our fellow human beings.

There is an alternative plan being formulated to take us sensibly into the next century.

This Book

If you'd like to know how you can help to make it succeed, perhaps add to it, or you are just curious to hear some alternative ideas, send a self addressed stamped envelope to the address you'll find at the front of "This Book".

* * * * *

As a foot note I should add that while prison seems to do little to prevent crime and might well add to it by what people learn from each other inside, people in prison in the U.K. in general are not treated badly and the staff are mostly helpful. There are education and other activities available for anyone wishing to make positive use of their time, and many positive and creative ideas are expressed and put into action, including many inmates and staff being involved in charity work.

STONED ON LIFE

Getting high is about experiencing reality from a different level and about feeling good.

As we have seen from our look at drugs there are many things which exist in our world which can alter the way people feel and look at things. Some carry with them unwanted side effects while others can be enjoyed with no real problems if used wisely.

We have seen how some drugs produce counterfeit endorphines which create a pleasurable sensation for the user. But our study would not be complete without a look at how the brain's own natural endorphines can be set loose without the use of drugs.

It is also possible to alter your consciousness of life with time honoured methods which involve no drugs at all.

In our next section we will explore a few of these.

287

Design by Dave Pace

MUSIC

What Is It?
The art of combining vocal
and instrumental sounds (or
both) producing beauty of
form, harmony, and expression of emotion.

Other Names:
Classical, Reggae, Blue Grass, Latin American, Calypso,
Medieval, Blues, Jazz, Rock and Roll, Rock, Heavy Metal,
Rap, Country, Middle of the road, Pop, House, Garage,
Jungle, Techno, Folk, Folk Rock, Techno Folk, Ballads,
and more.Each nationality have their own varieties as well.

Where Does It Come From?
The hearts and minds of people everywhere.

What Does It Cost?
From free, if you're singing in the shower, some optional
change if passing a busker, to the price of admission where
music is being played and if you're good at it, they might
even pay you to play.

Also available in recorded forms, vinyl, tape cassette and
CDs, approximately 45 minutes worth for between 5 and
16 pounds depending on the format and the popularity of
the performers.

Music

What Does It Do?
Depends on which form you use. Music can make you feel good, make you feel like dancing, make you laugh and make you cry.

Performing music for an audience from Karaoke on up to full scale concerts or raves is a real buzz.

Watching a good concert or attending a rave can leave you feeling good for ages after, and rehearing a song can bring back vivid memories of past times when you first heard the tune, (music flashback).

While playing music can involve complicated patterns and much practice on an instrument, it can also mean the simple tapping on a drum or the clapping of your hands in time. Hence it's something which nearly anyone can partake in if they wish.

It is difficult to find anything in this world which stirs the human emotions more than music can.

There are many people who go to raves simply to dance and enjoy the music, with no thought of taking drugs.

In our modern day with walkmans and car stereos, music can be enjoyed almost anywhere. While the beat can move your body sometimes the lyrics can feed your soul.

This Book

Music has always been an important part of every culture because it is such a good vehicle to express human feelings and emotions.

The party starts with the music, and ends when the music's over, (or when the Police confiscate the sound system).

PRECAUTIONS
Listening to music played too loud can do damage to your hearing.

Music should be listened to with consideration for others who may not share the same tastes.

The new criminal justice bill in the U.K. makes it illegal for ten people to gather and listen to music without a licence.

Grab an acoustic guitar, a tambourine and set of maracas to have a sing song in a field with a few friends and you could be arrested. Needless to say impromptu raves, parties, concerts or festivals are out of the question. And if you should decide you'd like to protest against this law, that's illegal too!

Author's Opinion
The next time you hear some birds singing in the trees, listen carefully, because at the rate these kill-joys are going that will soon be illegal too.

291

Don't let me catch you humming again!

TRANSCENDENTAL MEDITATION

What Is It?
A method of relaxation

Other Names:
T.M.

Where Does It Come From?
It has been passed down from Yogi to Yogi in India for countless years, to the Maharishi Mahesh Yogi who has set up a meditation teaching program making it available in many places round the world, (see your phone book for a centre near you).

What Does It Cost?
Prices vary according to your means. It may seem expensive, but then the benefits can last a lifetime.

What Does It Do?
It's like finding the pause button of your mind and using it twice a day to give it a rest.

Transcendental Meditation

The technique is quite specific and taught by people who have been well trained.

Scientific tests have shown that people reach a deep level of relaxation during meditation, much deeper than that reached in sleep.

The purpose of providing this apparent inactivity is to enable the mind to get on with all the jobs that it is normally too busy to do, such as repairing damage.

There are many doctors who recommend the use of T.M. to replace the need for tranquillisers and there is a campaign to make it generally available on the National Health, (At present this can only be approved in very special cases).

It is not in itself a religion and can be practiced by any one without the need to change their beliefs.

It is very simple to Meditate once you have been shown how, but then again most good things are simple.

By providing a welcome break to your mind, you give your thinking process a chance to work more clearly. Two twenty minute sessions can make a real difference to your day.

This Book

PRECAUTIONS
Learn from a qualified T.M. teacher and follow the instructions they give.

Transcendental Meditation is not the same as other forms of meditation.

Government's Opinion
While this natural method is proven to relieve stress and as a result effectively cures stress related complaints, the Government would rather spend huge amounts feeding people tranquillisers instead.

Author's Opinion
I've done T.M. for years. It's a good clean way to relax and I recommend it.

BUDDHISM

What Is It?
To some a philosophy of life.
To others a religion.

To those who practice it, it is life.

Other Names:
Zen, Theravada, Mahayana, are different schools of
Buddhism.

Where Does It Come From?
Within would be the obvious answer, however it originates
from North India which is now Nepal. It draws it's inspiration from a man named Siddhattha Gotama who lived and
taught some 2500 years ago and became known as the buddha which means the enlightened one.

Buddhism

What Does It Cost?
Nothing: Buddhist Centres will teach meditation for free. If you wish to stay at a centre, you could work for your board or make a small donation.

What Does It Do?
It's effects are unique to each person and can be found through meditation. It's main aim is to eliminate the desire and craving which leads to the unsatisfactoryness of life.

PRECAUTIONS
It can make you see things as they really are, eg. if you work in a slaughterhouse or in the arms trade, it may lead to a job change.

Government's Opinion
None at present,

(It has not dawned on our leaders that a fast growing religion based on genuine anti-war foundations could be a threat to a nation whose economy is based on the arms trade).

Users Opinion
To a Buddhist opinions are not that important as they are based on worldly things whereas we are more concerned with spiritual truths.

This Book

Author's Opinion

I'm not actually a Buddhist so I can comment here. Buddha taught peace and respect for all of life. He also taught that you reap what you sow, (what goes around comes around, Karma).

You don't need to be a Buddhist to be inspired by his teachings as the truth in them will compliment any real faith in good you may have.

Some of his stories are really fun and interesting with a moral that can give you a better view of life.

Why not plan a "Buddha Trip" through the London Buddhist Society by calling them on 071-834-5858 or by writing to them at 58 Eceleston Square, London SW1 to arrange a visit to a Buddhist Temple and broaden your horizons.

Special thanks to Robert Fairweather and Peter Taylor for the information they provided to help complete this section.

ART

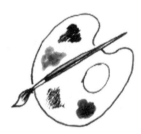

What Is It?
Various branches of creative activity concerned with the production of imaginative designs or ideas.

Other Names:
Painting, Sculpture (we mainly cover here, but can also include any creative activity)

Where Does It Come From?
There have been drawings found on stone walls believed to have been produced by cavemen.

It comes from creative minds with each nation having it's own form of original art.

Art

What Does It Cost?

The price of materials, which in the case of some sculpture can be junk acquired free, and the price of a teacher sometimes, which can vary.

What Does It Do?

The artist attempts to express a feeling through the thing which they create. They might reproduce a scene to convey the feeling of place, or they might create a design from their imagination to convey an abstract or a concrete idea. It can be anything from a simple emotion to the frustration felt before a revolution.

Being creative is fun, even if the thing you create means absolutely nothing to anyone else, however, if the feeling is conveyed successfully and others enjoy it, it's even more fun.

A painting or sculpture can continue to give joy or fascinate long after the artist's hand has left it. Creating an expressive work can therefore be very satisfying.

PRECAUTIONS

Don't underestimate your own creative ability.

A work of art can keep getting better until it starts to get worse. Learn when to stop.

If using power-tools take care.

This Book

Government's Opinion

There are art galleries to exhibit selected works, but if you decide to exhibit your sculptured concrete and scaffold pole car at a demonstration, such as the well publicised M11 extension protest (1994), be prepared to see your work destroyed by the establishment. In other words, Art is fine with them so long as it's fine with them.

Author's Opinion

Anyone can have fun doing paintings and sculptures, and if the work expresses the joy of making it, then that's a bonus.

Working with your hands to create interesting things to look at and enjoy is a very satisfying thing to do. Those with talent become obvious, (like our Max, who created all our cartoons), but you don't really need talent to produce interesting art. Sometimes just the right splash of paint can be really effective.

Sculptures can be made out of scrap material you can find in skips or around the house.

You'll be surprised what you can come up with if you give it a try. It's a nice way to spend a weekend, expanding your mind and imagination in a different way.

YOGA

What Is It?
Concentration and
training for body
and mind.

Other Names:
Ying and Yang -
The highest level

Where Does It Come From?
India where it is a living technique.

What Does It Cost?
Free, it can be learned in children's groups and family
weekends run by the British Wheel of Yoga, 1 Hamilton
Place, Boston Road, Sleaford, Lincs NG34 7ES who produce a quarterly program.

If you enjoy one of these free weekends and wish to be
more involved there is a fee set according to your means
with many classes up to and including qualifications to
become a teacher yourself.

What Does It Do?
Yogic teachers consider that the heart is like an engine.
The idea of Yoga is to slow down the rhythm of the heart.

Yoga

For example, the heart pumps about 10 tons of blood each 24 hour day, but if you breath in harmony the level can be reduced by a considerable percentage. The extra energy gained can then be used for the minds development. On a practical side, Yoga helps to keep away depressions, aggressions and fears. Yoga gives you possibilities to get deep relaxation, concentration and high energy. With Yoga it is claimed you can find yourself.

Each persons exercises are different to suit them, making the whole system of Yoga free. From children to old age, handicaps to fully fit any can benefit from Yoga. Yogic teachers are always aware of each students limitations and never push them beyond what will benefit.

Also: Yoga is about breathing into and out of the nose. The reason being that the little hairs in your nose cling, filtering out dirt while warming the air which is better for the lungs.

With Yoga breath is life. This special breathing can be practiced anywhere at any time and is very good at relieving stress.

PRECAUTIONS
Never go over your stretch point, because this is where the loss of concentration begins.

It is best to have a qualified teacher to start.

This Book

Government's Opinion
Totally banned and a Capital Offense (only kidding!).

While it is well established that practising yoga can lead to better health, the U.K. Government is reluctant to fund Yoga projects, seemingly set on using dangerous and sometimes addictive drugs to treat stress related problems.

Author's Opinion
The way in which the United Kingdom is run is a major cause of stress to the majority of people subjected to this management.

The government's lack of support for Yogic and meditation projects is a clear example of this. They spend Billions on a new trident missile project when the old one is still sitting there, good as new, never been used.

Far better it would be to spend money on good clean methods to health and relaxation. If they really cared about people instead of their own pockets then more positive things would be funded with the taxes they force us to pay them.

Yoga could be one of these positive things made available to everyone starting at school.

SPORTS

What Is It?
A game or competitive activity involving physical and/or mental exertion.

Other Names:
The Olympic Games (including all the competitions there). Various ball games such as; Soccer, Cricket, Baseball, American Football, Basket Ball, Bowls, and many more. Exploration sports such as mountain climbing, hiking, cave exploring, canoeing and boating which could be seen as games but are not necessarily competitive.

And a huge variety of unofficial sports, such as those seen on "Gladiators" T.V. show or at parties (which could include chess and various board games).

Sports

Where Does It Come From?
The Ancient Greeks are noted for holding the first
Olympics, but since the Dawn of Time people have been
pitting themselves against nature and each other. When this
is done in a positive non-harmful way we can call it sport.
So Sport comes from the roots of our civilisation and is
part of every nation's tradition.

What Does It Cost?
The price of the equipment needed and the playing space.
In the case of playing catch in your back yard or going for
a run, not much. In the case of race car driving, several
million pounds a year.

Many sports rely on sponsorship to survive, which means
the players wear brand names on their outfits in return for
equipment money received.

What Does It Do?
Being involved in Sports inspires people to get into top
physical shape so they can compete successfully. Pushing
your body to it's limits to be the best in an event can be a
real high, especially if you succeed.

Push your body beyond its normal limit and it will set
loose Endorphines and Adrenaline to make the experience
easier and more bearable. This rush of energy and pain
relief is known to be an enjoyable experience in itself.

Keep your eye on the ball

Sports

The term "Adrenaline Junkie" has been used to describe people hooked on this rush.

Since there are all types of sports, from the frantic to the really relaxed, most people can enjoy them and many people enjoy watching sports being played.

PRECAUTIONS
Get a checkup from you doctor before you start on any new training program or sporting activity.
Don't do too much too quickly. Build up your involvement a bit at a time, giving your muscles time to develop.

Be happy to play even if you loose, there's always next time.

Government's Opinion
This is something which they actively encourage, having international competitions as well as those on a national and local level.

Author's Opinion
Playing sports can be very good for you and provide a natural high. If competition between nations was limited to sports, we'd have no people dying in wars, which would obviously be a good thing.

TLC

What Is It?
"Tender Loving Care"

Other Names:
Kindness, love, good deeds,
charity work, Good Karma, a
helping hand, a shoulder to cry
on, care for animals, mercy, a kind word, being unselfish,
being forgiving, sharing and co-operation.

Where Does It Come From?

A loving heart.

What Does It Cost?
According to the law of Karma (That you reap what you
sow), whatever it costs will be refunded at a future date
when you need it.

What Does It Do?
Being a loving person in any situation which merits it, will
make you feel good.

Expressing love in any way will make you feel better about
yourself.

TLC

Many who have tried it say that expressing genuine unselfish tender loving care creates a real high which can't be compared to anything else.

Whether it's giving some change to a tramp, protesting against animal cruelty, standing in the way to stop a forest being destroyed by a new road, being a friend to someone in need, or just a kind word of encouragement to someone depressed, it's all meaningful and will leave you feeling good.

PRECAUTIONS.
Never underestimate what one person can do.

You don't need to join any clubs or organisations to feel the benefits of being kind.

Remember that little things matter. Small seeds can grow into big trees. Don't miss a chance to do good if you see one.

While it's true many have discovered that we do indeed "reap what we sow" in this world and "what goes around comes around", it often comes back later when we need it, and not from those we have helped.

Don't underestimate the power of sharing and co-operation. When you eat, the energy from the food gets shared round your body.

This Book

Without all your organs sharing with each other you would die.

Don't be afraid to ask if you are in need yourself. It could bring someone else joy to help you, and if they refuse you are no worse off.

Remember that Love is more than just romance and that each day affords you many opportunities to really care and feel the benefits of being kind.

Government's Opinion

All the major faiths in this world are based on the principles of Tender Loving Care. One of the corner stones of the Christian faith is the invitation for us to "love one another" and on the surface it would appear that the British government agrees with that principle, as they open their parliament with a prayer to the man who is said to have spoken those words.

But that man also taught that it was right to "ask and we would receive" and yet it is illegal for one person to ask another for coins in the street.

That same man is quoted as having said "blessed are the merciful for they shall obtain mercy" and mercy is indeed an attribute of Tender Loving Care, yet our legislators allow the hunting of foxes by blood thirsty dogs, and the transport of live animals for export, causing these innocent creatures to suffer needlessly for many hours and hundreds of miles.

And when a person tries to protest against this sort of unmerciful cruelty, they can be arrested for doing so.

The man these politicians pray to at the start of their sessions taught us to "love our enemies" but they use these sessions to prepare for war and vote for the funding of weapons designed for the mass destruction of other human beings.

Britain's Crown Prosecution Service proudly displays on it's crown the emblem of the man who taught us "not to judge" and "to forgive those who trespass against us" (a cross) while they set themselves up as Judges, keep a record of wrongs and never really forgive anyone.

Author's Opinion
re. The British Government:
They pray to one who taught only Tender Loving Care and would have us believe that this is a philosophy with which they agree, but their real opinion on the subject becomes clear when we observe what they do after saying that prayer.

re. TLC: it's what living is all about.

THE RAINBOW CONNECTION

What Is It?
An idealistic, futuristic, somewhat
mystically directed 'Power to the
People' movement - that has since
the autumn of 1984, been active on
the far out fringes of the British &
Irish political arenas with a view
towards assisting the creation of a
model 21st century society which aspires to
create peace and prosperity throughout The Cosmos.

Other Names:
Various connected elements are:
The Rainbow Dream Ticket Party
The Coming Out Party
Captain Rainbow's Universal Party (the mystical side)
The Outernet Project
The Knower's Arc Project
UNO, United Notions Organisation
The Brainbow Air Force
The Emerald Rainbow Islands Foundation
Fax Power '99 &TUFF (The Utopian Football Foundation)
Golden Rainbow Books
Message Parlour Records
The ... Out of This World 'J' Team

The Rainbow Connection

Where Does It Come From?
Nobody knows, but it evolved through the frequently stoned mind of a Lennonesque Dreamer known as Rainbow George - who lives in London & claims to be serving an apprenticeship under the mystical direction of an other worldly 'prophet' who he refers to as Sterling Silver, and belongs to all those who join in positive Rainbow activities.

What Does It Cost?
The price of the Dream Ticket for the rainbow Islands CD - advertised near the end of THIS BOOK.

The acquisition of this, Limited Sedition CD (only a million & one individually numbered copies) - entitles it's owners to free for life memberships of the Rainbow Dream Ticket Party & invites interaction with those associated in the "other names" section above.

What Does It Do?
The Rainbow Connection suggests an alternative to the way we live today.

It seeks to discover the ways & means required to raise Britain & Irish public awareness to such an extent that the good people of those two islands would come together to make the following written & recorded words come true.

An Apprentices Prophecy - December 1984:

Dear fellow traveller,

By the turn of this century we will all be handsomely rewarded for representing ourselves in a dream ticket democracy.

Soon the whistle is to be blown on the silly game we've been coerced into playing and those who we have allowed to exercise power and privilege will witness the demolition of their corrupt institutions.

Then, popular innovations will lead to our becoming a leisure orientated society whose standard of living and quality of life will be a beacon to the rest of the world.

Indeed, we shall enter the third millennium united in friendship as the people of the Emerald Rainbow Islands enjoying an idyllic environment free of poverty, fear, ignorance and debt.

Disturbing the comfortable, comforting the disturbed.

Yours happily inspired by a hopefully ,
Truthful Spirit   **Rainbow George**

The Rainbow Connection

What follows is only a brief outline of how the movement has developed.

Captain Rainbow's Universal Party entered the political arena in 1984 and has proven itself to have been at least 15 years ahead of it's time.

The Party, now evolved into the Rainbow Dream Ticket Party claims to represent the largest single group of people in the political arena, namely those who are sensible enough not to vote in parliamentary elections.

While other parties attempt to get elected into the present system, the Rainbow Connection candidates advocate The Abolition of Parliament and the introduction of power to the people.

The idea being that we could all vote directly on issues that concern us over the phone and cut out the money grabbing now obsolete politicians from the middle. Modern technology is now well enough developed to provide the presentation of ideas by experts in everyone's living room, and allow for intelligent decisions to be made by us for the common good of all.

In effect, voting for a Rainbow candidate is voting for a future in which you would represent yourself.

Rainbow George

The Rainbow Connection

In a model 21st century society - an agenda could be created that not only guarantees no bills for any of the basic necessities required for living a comfortable everyday life, but also offers chances of realistic occupations for everybody as part of this electronically interactive parliament.

Not without help from above, the "J" team, according to Stirling Silver, is led by risen stars such as; John Lennon and Judy Garland and also incudes Biblical Js from Joseph to Jesus, (rumour has it that every time a "J" is smoked the team becomes more powerful).

Not without a natural order, each community could be allowed to decide it's style and those attracted by that style could move to where they were best suited. This might result in a community of loud music lovers and another of quiet meditation, or even a community of pot smokers while others might focus on a drug free life style.

"Captain Rainbow" is the name that George has given to the character in the Bible referred to as "The Most High God" (who when mentioned by this name is never quoted as having said anything).

For the latest news you can check the web site on

www.rainbowparty.demon.co.uk

There are many events happening which you might enjoy being part of.

This Book

You'll recognise a Rainbow happening by the Rainbow "tick" like the one on the cover of "This Book"."Lets tick together" is the slogan of the rainbow movement, (as we count down to a better world).

There is nothing to stop you from having a Rainbow Happening of your own! (Let us know if you do.)

PRECAUTIONS
Always aim high. There is nothing more demoralising than aiming low and missing, and never forget that you are the star in your own life story.

Government's Opinion
The Rainbow Connection believe that the Government's Opinion is no longer relevant.

RAINBOW GEORGE'S OPINION
A short personal interview with the man himself.

Mike's Question: George, while it's true the Rainbow Connection addresses many serious issues, like the survival of life on this planet, some of it, like Stirling Silver the spaceman, and the "J" team seems like a bit of a send up, are you ever concerned that you might not be taken seriously?

George's Answer: No. I'd be more concerned if I was taken seriously, (slight grin). Italics Mike's observation

The Rainbow Connection

Mike's Question: What do you look forward to?

George's Answer: I look forward to a near future in which none of us will feel the need to take drugs as a means of escape but rather as means of participation and discovery, but most I look forward to a day when we could ask "Is everybody happy?" and everyone would say "YES".

Mike's Question: What are your views on prison and people convicted of drug dealing?

George's Answer: The movement advocates an amnesty for all convicted prisoners who don't pose a physical threat to society, and compensation for all dealers of non-addictive drugs, as their only crime was to try to bring a bit more joy into the world.

Mike's Question: Can you tell me a bit about Captain Rainbow and what you feel his views might be on this subject?

George's Answer: Yes I can. I perhaps mischievously believe The Most High God, (Captain Rainbow), owes his official Biblical title to the Grass that supposedly grows in Rainbowland. (picture on page 253 perhaps?)

Mike's Question: George, thank you for taking the time to be with us. To close is there anything you would like to say to our readers?

George's Answer: Yes, The Rainbows Are Coming!!!

THE RAINBOWS ARE COMING
by Rainbow George

ALTHOUGH YOU'VE PROBABLY FORGOTTEN, NOW IS THE
HOUR FOR YOU TO WAKE UP AND TUNE INTO THE
RAINBOW CONNECTION- COME ON WAKE UP!
WAKE UP!

The Rainbows are coming to right all wrongs - to
awaken the world with Rainbow songs - to encour-
age we earthlings to do our duty - to restore this
planet to its erstwhile beauty
Chorus;
So be of good cheer - have no fear
Try to remember why we're all here
Just open your eyes see love is the prize
Feel for a minute - together we'll win it

The Rainbows are coming to lend a hand - to light-
en the way to a Rainbow land - Warriors of an
ancient tribe - tuned into the now age vibe
Chorus

The Rainbows are coming to ring our bells - to
release us from our prison cells - building bridges -
breaking down walls - Happiness beckons -
Destiny calls.
Chorus

The Rainbows are coming for me and you
The Rainbows are coming to make our dreams
come true.

The Rainbow Connection

Author's Opinion

How many people do you know who are actively working full time to change the world for the better? Rainbow George is such a person. I've known George since the start of his campaign, and while I appreciate that some of his ideas might seem a bit far out, there is no denying his genuine perseverance towards his positive goals. Rainbow events are always good fun.

The idea that machines can do most of the needed work for us is turned from a curse into a blessing with George's ideas.

Real progress has up to now been opposed by those who fear they will lose their jobs in its wake.

The Party is not afraid to redefine our purpose in life. We struggle because we fear we will not get paid if we don't. George's proposition to make each person responsible for themselves and paying them to do the job might seem unrealistic in our present day society, and it probably is unrealistic with the way things are now, but change society and the way things are and who can say what our limitations will be?

George predicts "Indeed, we shall enter the third millennium united in friendship as the people of the Emerald Rainbow Islands enjoying an idyllic environment free of poverty, fear, ignorance and debt."

This Book

Very late in 98, as I prepared the proofs for this second edition, the chances of George's 14 year old prediction coming true seemed pretty remote.

However after visiting George the Sunday following Boxing Day, his continued optimism lead me to think the odds were better than even. After all, what he predicts is not something any of us could sanely vote against, is it. Is it true "when enough people imagine something wonderful and wish it to happen...it happens"? This is what the rainbow connection has been attempting to test.

What constitutes "enough people"? As far as George is concerned this could be 72,000 people or so dream ticket carrying football fans in an 'All Change For The 21st Century' concert event which could take place at Wembley Stadium. An event that would not only help lay Utopian Foundations for footballs future but also announce the emergence of the movements 'Coming Out Party" to stand in the June 99 European Election, allowing British People for the first time to vote to "come out" of Europe and allow individuals the opportunity to govern themselves, instead of being dictated to by the Brussels Gravy Train.
(Or 100,000 people at **THE CONCERT** in Amsterdam?)

For these any other reasons "Rainbow' George was looking forward to a year of signs and wonders and maybe...just maybe 1999 would indeed prove to have been The Year of the Rainbows.

The Rainbow Connection

George, like John Lennon, invites us to imagine a better world and he believes if enough of us do so, it can become a reality.

He is a fine example of an individual using his imagination to the full in a positive way which is what has earned the Rainbow Connection it's place in "This Book".

DARE TO DREAM... AND YOUR DREAMS MIGHT COME TRUE!

In Rainbowland there will be
neither need nor greed,
Or any use for silly money
No politicians, no preachers,
No incompetent teachers,
No ignorant views,
No business to lose.
No corrupt institutions
Or harmful pollutions,
Not a trace of sadness,
One world,
No divisions,
Everybody involved in
reaching decisions,
Free of hypocricy,
A genuine democracy.

In Rainbowland there will be
neither need nor greed,
Or any use for silly money,
No poverty, no hunger,
The old grow younger
No shedding of blood
Or slinging of mud,
Nor wicked wheezes,
Or any diseases,
The blind will see,
The deaf will hear,
The lame will run,
The dumb will cheer,
Infinite variety,
nothing to rue,
A joyous society,
where wishes come true.

CHORUS

I'm not sure how,
and I don't know when,
What's now is now,
Yet it won't be then,
As far as the eagle's eye can see,
The futures bright
for you and me,
Mark my words,
Losers will win
Beggars will choose,
Wars will cease,
We're going to play in peace,
Dreamy views.
What else is news?

In Rainbowland there will be
Neither need nor greed,
Or any use for silly money,
A Magical Place,
Full of style and grace,
Wondrous sights and sounds
Wisdom abounds.
Though you may not believe it,
Please try to perceive it,
Imagine our world designed
for pleasure,
With science and art
a combination to treasure
Just wait and see,
We'll be living free,
Whatsoever our fate,
Our destiny is great....

SEX

What Is It?
Probably the most sought after natural buzz in the world.

It is the stimulation of sexual organs to Orgasm.

Other Names:
Making Love, Intercourse, Fucking, Getting Laid, Balling, A Blow Job, Going Down, Mutual Masturbation, Solo Masturbation, Wanking, and many other variations on the theme.

Where Does It Come From?
It is a natural function that has been around as long as life has.

What Does It Cost?
The best things in life are free, but with some people the price of sex is negotiable.

What Does It Do?
On a biological level it provides the means for living things to procreate.

Sex

On a casual level it can be a means of fun and excitement.

On a romantic level it can be the expression of love and affection.

On a serious level it can be the basis of a meaningful relationship, and the means of creating a family, which can be romantic and exciting as well.

Misused it can be the source of heartache and even the cause of disease and sometimes death.

PRECAUTIONS

The usual advice is wear a condom or dental doms to prevent the other person's fluids from entering your body, and to stop your fluids from entering theirs. Reason being that the fluids might contain a disease you could catch or give, (AIDS), and to prevent unwanted pregnancy.

Also only use water based lubricants like KY or Jelly, as oil can cause condoms to tear. Check condoms are not out of date and that they are kite marked.

While the mechanics of this advice is sound if you intend to partake in full penetration sex, the concentration on this aspect leaves little room for imagination. There are lots of ways you can make your partner happy and bring them to Orgasm without the risk of catching AIDS or becoming pregnant, which don't involve full penetration.

This Book

These can be an exiting adventure in their own right.

Being careful might mean finding a new texture as a lubricant or even sharing the use of a sex aid. It doesn't have to be all the way to be memorable or fun. The place you do it in can add as much to the excitement as the way you do it.

HIV is the main concern here, because HIV+ is a possible death sentence.

So you've found someone you really care for and you'd like to fuck them silly. HIV can take three months to show up with a test. You've both been with other people and you are not sure. Why not explore all the other things you can do for three months then go for a test a deux, (that's test for two). If nothing shows on the test then you can fuck each other silly to celebrate.

If one is HIV+ then the other can decide if they want to risk their life on the strength of thin rubber. If both are HIV+ there's nothing to lose, (make the most of it while you still can).

Because Aids can kill you it's a really serious thing. A moment of pleasure is not worth risking your life for.

The older generation's answer is to recommend using a condom, because for the most part they don't believe that young people can be sensible or imaginative with their sex lives.

Sex

While it's true to say that using a condom while having full sex can protect you most of the time, using your imagination with your partner to find other ways and interesting places will protect you completely and can be just as much fun.

It's worth noting that condoms (and dental doms) are much less likely to break during oral sex, if they do you'll notice right away so you can stop, and the dangers of disease transmition are lower with this method to begin with.

If you are one of the growing number who would rather wait until you are married to have sex, then that's up to you, but whether you are married or not, being faithful to your partner and protecting them from risk is always the caring thing to do.

Also if there is no-one there to love you, there's nothing wrong with loving yourself.

Government's Opinion
A good effort has been made to make people aware of the dangers of AIDS. The push of publicity is aimed at encouraging people to use condoms with little imagination.

If one is to believe the News of the World some Members of Parliament have very bizarre sexual habits.

This Book

Author's Opinion

Little is said about the risk of condoms breaking. They do, sometimes. I'm not being a stick in the mud here, I'm just telling it as it is. Hearing about AIDS and then being told to wear a condom can give the impression that full penetration sex is the only kind worth having and that condoms are completely safe.

Perhaps politicians and some parents are too shy to tell their daughters, "when your boy friend gets horny and wants to take you to bed, why not cover your hand with some baby oil from your purse, loosen your blouse and reach down his jeans". Now being realistic, do you really think the young man would object to that? (and it would certainly put paid to the old "if you love me you wouldn't leave me so frustrated" moan). I'm for encouraging young people to care, using their imaginations and taking NO risks.

How many dads do you know who are suggesting to their sons that they might invest in a vibrator to surprise their girlfriend? More expensive than a condom but they never break causing death. I could go on, but you get the idea.

Amuse each other safely and if you find three months have passed and you've just been amusing each other exclusively, have an HIV test. If nothing shows up you can expand your range of experience, using the pill if you're concerned about having kids.

THE HOLY SPIRIT OF LIFE

What Is It?
The energy of life which flows in all living things and the power that keeps atoms spinning and makes all things possible.

Other Names:
The Great Spirit of the Cosmos, the Force, The Comforter, the Spirit of Truth, the Spirit of Christ, the Spirit of Love, the Power of Sharing and Co-operation.

337

The Holy Spirit Of Life

Where Does It Come From?
It doesn't come from anywhere, everything comes from it.
Many believe that its' love for mankind was and is perfectly expressed in the life of Jesus Christ.

What Does It Cost?
Real love is always free and anything you might do to prepare yourself to receive it is always part of the gift. "Lots of gifts come with instructions and they wouldn't be complete without them. Still you're not likely to feel you are paying for a gift simply because you are using it properly".

What Does It Do?
The Holy Spirit of Life is a Loving Power. It reacts to all things in a loving way. Love is met with love. Error is met with correction and forgiveness. Fear is met with comfort and faith, and faith is met with completion and knowledge. In short, it forgives the past, provides faith for the future, and inspires love for every thing now.

It maintains the flow of life, giving us the chance to discover and experience its' wonder.

It inspires the creation of all music and art. It is the vibe that ravers dance to. It is the destination of all those who really get high.

Everyone experiences it, but not all realise what it is when they do.

338

PRECAUTIONS
Beware of organisations which claim to represent The Holy Spirit but act in unloving ways.

Government's Opinion
Elected officials spend most of their time doing things to make up for their lack of faith in the Holy Spirit, (like priming bombs and building prisons).

As for the House of Lords, instead of believing in the Lord, they call themselves lords and believe in themselves. It is fairly amazing how such a pageantry of contradictions is ever taken seriously by anyone.

Authors Opinion
Organised religion is largely responsible for obscuring the beauty which is everyone's birthright.

As the missionaries could not see that the American Indians had found a natural understanding of the real Holy Spirit, so today, the real love and joy experienced by dancing ravers is seen by the establishment as something apart from the truth and something they feel the need to stop or control.

Good News or Bad News?

"THAT BOOK"

What Is It?
It is a non-religious, spiritual philosophy book for young people and the young at heart, (pocket sized like "This Book" 162 pages long).

Other Names:
The Things They Don't Teach You in School

Where Does It Come From?
I wrote it, and this a plug for it. It is available mail order from "Those Publishers", P.O. Box 10059 London NW2 6WR or from any bookshop. It's also free on the net in 6 different languages at:

www.netmatters.co.uk/users/startingout

That Book

What Does It Cost?
£3.95 from here, including postage and packing, £4.95 in shops or free on the net.

What Does It Do?
It can give you a completely new outlook on life if you read it carefully with an open mind. If you've enjoyed some of the social comments and positive ideas in "This Book", then you will love "That Book, The Things They Don't Teach You in School". It has been described as being "like a trip without drugs", (Rave Magazine 1990). (For your convenience there is an order form at the end of "This Book" you can use.)

PRECAUTIONS
Do not leaf through it. Take the time to read it carefully.
It defines itself as you read so reading the end first can be confusing and give the wrong impression.

Government's Opinion
No official comment yet, but I have seen a government document which refers to it as anti-establishment.

Author's Opinion
"That Book" took me 18 months to write. Hearing from people who have really understood it makes me realise that this was time well spent. I hope you order a copy and then maybe I'll hear from you.

SHEDDING SOME LIGHT IN THE DARK

"IN CLOSING"

Our list of natural highs is far from complete. There are loads of things we could add, like creative writing, all forms of crafts, travel, and even daydreaming, but we have covered enough I hope, to give you the general idea. Life is full of opportunities to enjoy it.

As for Drugs, while there are people living on Earth, drugs will continue to be taken.

Drug taking is not something that will ever be stopped by using force, and the most we can hope for is for people who take drugs to be sensible.

Shedding Some Light In The Dark

The day that governments first tried to tell us what we should and should not put into our bodies was the day they crossed an unacceptable line. To give advice on what they think is good or bad is one thing. To attempt to force their tastes on us is quite another.

What you decide to take into your body is no-one else's business but your own.

They are attempting to exercise authority within an area in which they have no jurisdiction. And this may well lead us to ask, what right have they got to exercise any authority at all whatsoever?

Throughout "This Book" I have pointed to the American Indians as an example of a people who had a sensible attitude towards drugs. The Indians did not try to separate drugs from life. To them all good gifts came from the Great Spirit and things were to be enjoyed in their season.

Strawberries grew from plants, the same as Peyote. Each made you feel good in their own way when you ate them.

If a new part of nature revealed itself with Peyote, the Indian did not try to ban it, he did not try to destroy it, he did not run away. He faced the new reality he was experiencing with anticipation of the gifts it might bring. He looked for meaning in the things that he saw and sought things that might make him a better person.

This Book

This was not a drug to him, some alien thing for him to fear and despise; it was just a plant, a plant with a message which grew from the ground. He picked it when he needed it. He had no stash, no locked doors and there were no drug dealers in his society.

And if by chance he ate something with which his system did not agree, and it made him ill with no good feelings at all, he might tell his friends that this plant was to be avoided; and they would believe him without any need to use force. Helpful information not vindictive legislation.

In an attempt to justify the drug laws, real information is suppressed and as a result there are many people who don't even know the difference between Ecstacy and Heroin.

A friend of mine was recently asked by a government official how he had managed the "Cold Turkey" from stopping use of Ecstacy. He was hard pressed to explain that one does not suffer "Cold Turkey" when one stops using "E".

The lady was surprised to hear this, but how much more surprised do you think she might be if she started suffering from withdrawals herself, while trying to stop taking the tranquillisers her doctor has prescribed? "Just a little something to help relieve the stress, my dear lady"

The style of our present leaders is to try to impose their will on others by force.

Shedding Some Light In The Dark

I strongly believe that such methods should be opposed by decent people, not by using force in return, but by using information. That is the spirit in which "This Book" has been written.

The drugs issue is one which is riddled with misinformation. If "This Book" has helped to shed some light on the subject for you perhaps you'll consider passing it on to a friend.

Its been a pleasure talking to you, till next time,
Be sensible and have fun . . .

Help Spread the Word &
Win a Free A3 Colour Poster

What to do:

1. Tell a friend about THIS BOOK. (One Point)

2. Mention THIS BOOK on a radio talk show.
(Three Points)

3. Have your library order a copy. (Two Points)

4. Write to your local paper about THIS BOOK.
(Two Points) if published (Three Points)

5. Ask a bookshop if it's in stock. (One Point)

It's Easy to WIN

Just earn three points, then send your name,
address & a second class stamp to:
Free Poster P.O. Box 10059, London NW2 6WR

Remember: It's more fun when you've really won!

This Book

INDEX

Index

This Book

Index

This Book

Index

This Book

Index

This Book

YOU'VE READ THIS,

NOW READ THAT!

HAVE YOU HEARD ???

On May 20th 1990, something special happened. A cheerful brightly coloured paperback book came onto the market. It is simply called "THAT BOOK". Many agree there has never been a book like it. Since it's introduction thousands of copies have been read and it's popularity continues to grow.

It's difficult to explain what "THAT BOOK" is all about in a few words, but once you've read it you will understand and want your friends and family to read it to. It's only a short book, yet it's 162 pages contains more thought provoking material than most books many times it's length. It makes you feel good about being alive, and answers questions you have been wondering about in such a way even a young child can understand it.

"THAT BOOK" belongs in the 21st century. It is a signpost to our future and a reminder of what we really can be.

PTO

THIS IS THE ONE THE WORLD HAS BEEN WAITING FOR!

Now is your chance to discover it for yourself! "THAT BOOK" will not appear out of thin air, so you'll have to do as thousands have before you and use one of the order forms opposite. It's all part of the fun. **DO IT NOW!**

If the order forms in this book have already been used simply send your name and address and £3.95 *cheque or postal order* payable to Those Publishers, P.O Box 10059 London NW2 6WR with the words "THAT BOOK" on a piece of paper.

YOU'LL BE GLAD YOU DID.

PLEASE send me my copy of
THAT BOOK
I enclose £3.95 payable to:-
THOSE PUBLISHERS
P.O. Box 10069
London NW2 6WR

NAME ....
ADDRESS ....
....
....
POST CODE ....

PLEASE send me my copy of
THAT BOOK
I enclose £3.95 payable to:-
THOSE PUBLISHERS
P.O. Box 10069
London NW2 6WR

NAME ....
ADDRESS ....
....
....
POST CODE ....

XAT

A Brief History of Money
& The Model for
A Tax Free Economy

A New Book by Mike Rock
In Bookshops Now
or
£4.95 mail order from

Those Publishers
P.O. Box 10059
London NW2 6WR

You People

It's plain that you're an awful shower
You people to whom we've given power
Aspiring to lord us from some lofty tower
The clocks are ticking towards your final hour.

chorus:
We don't trust you
we don't want you
we don't need you any more
so we're making you redundant
we're showing you the door

Whistles shall be blown on your silly games
your best laid plans will go up in flames
The Rainbows are coming to
stake their claims
You people will do well to now change your aims.

chorus:
We don't trust you
we don't want you...etc

You people
champions of hypocrisy
corruption and deceit
Think the ways you fool us
are really rather neat
Yet our island's good people
are about to perform a feat
one way or another
we're all in for a treat.

chorus:
We don't trust you
we don't want you...etc